375
144

Also by Lee Hastings Bristol, Jr.

HYMNS FOR CHILDREN AND GROWNUPS
Co-edited with Harold W. Friedell

Seed for a Song

Portrait by Raymond L. Grass

RT. REV. ROBERT NELSON SPENCER, D.D., LL.D.

Seed for a Song

BY

Lee Hastings Bristol, Jr.

LITTLE, BROWN AND COMPANY

Boston   Toronto

The author wishes to thank the following for permission to include copyrighted material in his book:

The Right Reverend Robert Nelson Spencer and The Church Pension Fund for quotations from several poems and hymns by Bishop Spencer.

Harper & Brothers for a prayer from THE REDEEMER by Robert Nelson Spencer and for the poem "Well?" by G. A. Studdert-Kennedy from this author's UNUTTERABLE BEAUTY.

Charles Scribner's Sons for a quotation from THE SEER'S HOUSE by Robert Nelson Spencer.

TO THE MEMORY OF

ELIZABETH WIGTON BRISTOL

WHOSE LIFE WAS HER MAGNIFICAT

I went down into the ground to grow,
A seed for a song that would make men know.

— From *Eye-Witness*
by Ridgely Torrence

Contents

Seed for a Song

CHAPTER I

How the Accident Happened

THE ACCIDENT OCCURRED one bitter cold, sunny morning in February of 1884. The upstate countryside around Tunnel, New York, was under three feet of snow, and a sleet storm the night before had left a smooth, glassy crust on the steep slope at the back of the Spencer farm, where boys from the neighboring farms liked to go sledding.

As soon as the breakfast dishes had been dried and stacked, young Robbie Spencer hurried into the front room to look out and watch the road for Mert Owens and John Brown to appear with their sleds.

Little Robbie had just turned seven, and his father, Nelson Spencer, had made him a new sled for his birthday from oak planks he had been saving in the barn. Robbie had purposely left the sled out front where the two older boys would be sure to see it as they approached the house. The sled was very sturdy, as Robbie's father had made two wooden runners, fastened them with "rounds" like the braces on the legs of a chair, then nailed a wide oak plank across the top. It seemed to Robbie as hard to pull uphill as a canalboat, but it did make time on the orchard slope.

It was not long before Robbie spotted the boys who lived near by coming across the snow. By the time they reached the front steps, Robbie was bundled up in his thick, quilted coat and out on the porch to greet them.

"When did you get the sled?" Mert asked.

"It's wonderful, Robbie!" said John.

Robbie beamed. "Father made it for me for my birthday. It's solid oak. Watch! I can even jump on it." Robbie demonstrated by jumping up and down on the sled.

"Sure is a strong one," said Mert, as the three boys, pulling their sleds, went around the side of the house back toward the orchard slope, which ran as far as the railroad fence some distance from the house. The apple trees were spaced far apart and the slope was steep enough so that boys could coast nearly half a mile in the one direction.

All morning, the boys raced each other down the slope. Mert was leading, having won sixteen races to the other boys' ten.

They started down once more. One of the boys took off first. Robbie was second. They were going like the wind when Robbie's sled hit a hummock of ice and he was thrown skidding across the icy crust. Unfortunately, the third sled was on him in a second. One of the flashing runners ran like a knife across his arm.

Robbie was just able to get to his feet and go back to the house under his own steam, but the two older boys went with him. There was no more sledding for Robbie that day, for his arm began to swell.

At first, Robbie's mother thought it just another minor childhood mishap; sledding mishaps were common enough on an upstate farm. Her older children — Guy, Irving, Nettie — had all had their share.

Several days passed, however, and Robbie's swollen arm showed no improvement.

"Robbie, does it feel any better?" Hannah kept asking hopefully.

"Mother, it hurts. It really hurts."

Nelson beckoned to his wife to follow him into the other room.

"Hannah, what do you think?" he said, closing the door behind them.

"His arm looks terribly bruised and sore to me. He winches whenever I try to touch it."

"Do you think the swelling has gone down any?"

"No, I don't. If anything, it looks worse."

Nelson looked very sober. "Hannah," he said, "I'm going for Doc Beardsley."

"I guess you'd better," said Hannah.

Calling the doctor was an unusual procedure for the Spencers. "It's not fair to bother him," Hannah would often say. "Doc Beardsley has to cover too much territory as it is. He has thirty square miles full of sicker people than us to take care of."

As soon as he could get away, which was not until about sundown, Nelson set out to find the doctor. Hannah stayed behind with Robbie, who was lying on the soft old sofa beside the fire. His mother tucked a couple of cushions under his arm.

"There, does that feel any better?" she asked.

"Maybe, just a little."

"Would you like a little something to eat?"

Robbie tried to force a smile. "Not right now, Mother, thanks."

It was several long hours before they heard the welcome sound of the sleighs approaching. Hannah's face lighted up as she heard the two men stamping their feet on the porch to shake the snow off their boots.

Robbie's father and the doctor came in quietly. Doc Beardsley nodded to Hannah and the pale young patient on the couch.

"What's this I hear about the perils of sledding?" he said, smiling.

Doc Beardsley always exuded a kind of quiet confidence which was very reassuring to his patients. No wonder we all love him! Hannah thought.

He walked over to the fire, hung his heavy coat over the back of a chair, and pulled off his boots, which were still somewhat caked with snow. Then he sat down beside Robbie on the couch.

"And how's our invalid?" he asked.

"Just fine," Robbie said unconvincingly.

"Tell me just how it happened, Robbie."

Robbie told him and ended his story with a now familiar complaint: "Doctor, it hurts, it really hurts bad."

"I'm sure it does," said Doc Beardsley sympathetically.

"Luckily, he had on his thick, quilted coat," said Hannah. "I think that must have protected him some."

Doc Beardsley examined the swollen little arm for some minutes in silence.

"What do you think, Doctor?" Hannah asked, finally.

"I don't know, Hannah," said the doctor. "Could I talk to you and Nelson in the kitchen for a minute?" He led the way.

"My friends," he said, closing the door behind him, "I don't like the looks of Robbie's arm. There's pus there.

It is badly swollen and inflamed, as you can see, and I'm afraid I've got to lance it."

"Will it hurt him terribly?" Hannah asked anxiously.

"Hannah, I'll do it as quickly as I can."

They went back to the living room. When Robbie saw the doctor fish in his black bag for the instruments and noticed how quiet his parents were, he became frightened. Hannah stroked his forehead gently to comfort him, and he relaxed a little under her touch.

"I'll need a little more light," said the doctor.

"Here's a lantern. I'll put it on the chair," Nelson said.

The doctor leaned over to Robbie. "Now this will hurt some, my boy, but I'll be as quick as I can."

Then came the quick, sharp stroke of the knife. Robbie let out a shriek. Hannah put her hands over her face as blood gushed from her son's arm.

"But there is no pus!" the doctor exclaimed in astonishment.

Hannah rushed into the other room and returned with an armful of clean rags to sop up the blood and dress the wound.

The doctor had not realized that a number of blood vessels in the upper arm had been ruptured, as a result of which a hematoma had developed which gave the arm the appearance of being swollen with pus. When the doctor lanced the swelling, he merely created an opening through which the secondary, or chronic, infection was to establish itself.

The doctor had no way of predicting that Robbie's arm would soon stiffen to his side and remain so for many years, or that in a few days, fine splinters of bone would begin to force their way to the surface to be pulled out like needles. He could not foresee that this condition would become systemic, and that, in a few weeks, bone slivers would begin to appear in the left ankle as well.

When Doc Beardsley left at last, neither he nor the Spencers realized what suffering lay ahead for the little boy. Robbie's throbbing arm had a fresh dressing on it. Nelson saw the doctor to his sleigh and thanked him warmly again for coming the long distance. Somehow, he felt that, with the good doctor's care, all would be well. He picked up the rope on Robbie's sled and towed it slowly away to the barn.

CHAPTER II

Long Hours under the Stove

ROBBIE, OR ROBERT NELSON SPENCER as he was later baptized, was born, during a snowstorm, in the isolated Spencer farmhouse in Broome County, New York, on February 18, 1877. The snow was fence-high at the time. The Spencers never knew how the old country doctor, traveling through the drifts by dogcart and dobbin, managed to beat the stork, traveling by air. Robbie was the youngest of four living children born to Hannah and Nelson Horatio Spencer. Another child had died in infancy.

Robbie's family consisted of Irving, a lanky young man already in his teens; Guy, who was then seven years old; and Nettie Eleanor, who was three.

The post office address read Tunnel, New York, after the two-hundred-and-twenty-two-foot tunnel which the Delaware and Hudson Canal Company had burrowed through the hill there on its way from Albany to Binghamton. Tunnel was two miles from the Spencer farm and boasted a population of about twenty people. There was a general store which also served as post office, a creamery where local farmers took their milk, and a few houses which sheltered the residents against the bitter upstate winters.

Tunnel had enjoyed its one historic moment several years before when the famous "Battle of the Tunnel" took place — the struggle for possession of a railroad then called the Albany and Susquehanna. Jay Gould and Jim Fisk, who controlled the Erie, were determined to acquire the Albany and Susquehanna as well. Joseph H. Ramsey, President of the Albany and Susquehanna, was prepared to fight; he marshaled his forces, and set out with them for Tunnel.

The Fisk locomotive, pulling flatcars full of railroad men armed with pickaxes, left Binghamton at top speed and headed for Tunnel. At the same time, Ramsey's locomotive, also pulling flatcars of strong and determined men, was rushing toward Tunnel from the other direction. The Fisk forces reached the tunnel first, passed through it and out the other side, careened around a sharp curve, and met the Ramsey engine head-on. The two locomotives came together with a great crash at the point where the two railroads intersected near the foot of the Spencer farm. There were no casualties, but the opposing forces found themselves with a considerable amount of crumpled iron on their hands. The 44th Regiment of the New York State Militia stepped in before further harm was done, and despite the craftiness of their efforts in the months to come, Gould and Fisk failed to take from Ramsey his control of the railroad.

Rolling hills and valleys surrounded Tunnel. In fact, Nelson Spencer's one-hundred-and-ten-acre farm was mostly hillside. The soil was very poor, and he had to earn his income mainly from the cows.

The Albany and Susquehanna tracks cut right across the farm, and Nelson had to drive his cows through a culvert under the railroad to get them down to the far pasture. As the children grew older, this became one of their jobs. Robbie eagerly looked forward to the day when he could get to drive the cows through the culvert all by himself.

The Spencers learned through hardship how best to stretch the few dollars they earned from the farm. Hannah was forever showing her resourcefulness in the way she helped them cut corners. She and Nelson allowed themselves coffee only on Sundays, and the children's clothes were made to be passed along and to last as long as Hannah's mending would permit.

The Spencers lived in a well-built old frame house. Counting Robbie's attic room, there were six bedrooms upstairs. Downstairs there was a large kitchen with a modestly stocked "cold room" where food was stored, a living room which also served as a dining room, and a formal parlor which was reserved for only the most special occasions.

A library of "bound books" lined the walls of the parlor. Nelson often told his children how proud they should be of this distinction, for not many farm families boasted such a library. At times Nelson would read some famous dramatic passage aloud to the children — with all the fervor of a traveling tragedian — but it was soft-spoken Hannah who knew the books best and who would regularly read aloud in the evening.

Irving, the oldest son, seemed genuinely devoted to his younger brothers and sister and went out of his way to include them in whatever he did. One cloudy afternoon, when Robbie was only four, Irving took the boy on an errand to a neighbor. On the way home they were caught in a torrential downpour. The sound of the heavens bursting overhead terrified Robbie. He clung to Irving and could not hold back his tears.

Irving immediately picked his brother up in his arms and carried him. As they neared the house, Robbie stopped crying.

"I'm not scared now," he said, in a quavering voice. "See, I even made up a poem about the storm:

> It is raining down from Heaven
> In the Inger, Inger sea."

Neither Irving nor anyone else ever heard of the "Inger, Inger sea," but the whole family congratulated their young poet at supper that evening when Irving asked him to repeat the little poem.

"You'll have to write an epic poem someday about the Civil War," said Nelson, who liked nothing better, himself, than to declaim about the war on state occasions.

Robbie's earliest years were full of good times with Guy and Nettie and Irving. Like any typical farm family in Broome County, winters meant skating, sledding, pillow fights, evenings before the fire, and school. In summer the Spencer family virtually lived outdoors. They divided their time between swimming, fishing, building a tree house perhaps, and helping their father with chores.

Robbie's accident changed everything: it forced the little boy off to the side lines.

As the arm stiffened to his side, Robbie was more and more forced to curtail his activities. At first, his parents thought he was at least well enough to go two miles up the road to the Millers' School, a small red building which stood on a hill overlooking the nearby meadows, called so because it stood directly across from the Millers' farm. Robbie tried his best to keep up with the other children, but inevitably some boy or girl would accidentally jostle him, and bring on another painful hemorrhage. Again and again, some teacher had to take the little boy home, his shirt drenched with blood.

We have had to take him out of school [Hannah wrote her cousin later that year]. Poor little chap, he longs to be at school with the others. It is a heartache to see him staring out the window as Nettie and Guy leave for school in the morning. Why did this have to happen to Robbie? What ever will he do when he grows up? Cousin Margaret, sometimes I find my faith wavering a bit. Then I am with the boy a few minutes. I see the bravery in those bright little eyes as I draw out the small bone slivers from his arm, and I have courage that somehow Robbie will find his way.

Day after day, Hannah would bathe the sore arm, perhaps draw out another splinter of bone, and apply a homemade dressing made from long strips of linen or wool scraps from her mending bag. Robbie might limp around in the field back of the house, but his arm remained bound to his side and the least injury brought on another hemorrhage.

Heat was the one thing which seemed to ease his pain. Once Robbie discovered he could wriggle his way under the stove and lie there comfortably for hours. This spot became a favorite retreat for the boy. Often, of a morning, one would find Hannah reading the Bible aloud in her Boston rocker in the kitchen while Robbie listened intently from under the stove. Hannah had not had much schooling, but she was well read and wrote a beautiful hand. When she read aloud in her clear, simple way,

Robbie could listen by the hour. She did not read with all the affected resonance of Nelson, who fancied himself a kind of orator, but she liked to read great poetry from the "bound books" or long passages from the Bible or Prayer Book, and Robbie liked nothing better than to listen to the beautiful words in his mother's voice.

In those days, too, Robbie might spend long hours up in his attic room, sprawled out on a mattress bulging with corn husks. There he would lie, wondering about the years ahead or simply listening to the wind in the trees or the rain which played on the roof.

In the years which followed, there was little to break the monotony of Robbie's life. His mother did teach him to read a little for himself, and he could quote from memory a good many passages from the Bible which he had heard Hannah read in the kitchen. One day, his mother caught him out by the barn, dressed in Nelson's Sunday coat, delivering a funeral sermon for a small dead bird he had buried in a little box.

"For what is your life?" Hannah heard the young orator say in the words of the Bible. "It is even a vapour, that appeareth for a little time, and then vanisheth away."

"What somber words for a little boy!" she said, bursting into tears as she ran toward him. "Robbie," she said, hugging him tightly, a new hope springing into her mind, "maybe, someday, you will be a preacher!"

But railroading seemed dearer to the lonely boy's heart, and many an afternoon Hannah would catch sight of him down at the end of the orchard slope, leaning over the fence to watch the 4:04 go by.

During this period, Nelson was very active in the G.A.R. Association and was faithful about attending meetings, even though it meant traveling some seven miles down the railroad track to Harpursville, and leaving his family alone.

In those days tramps were forever following the railroad tracks. Often, as the sun began to go down, some weary tramp would wander up the orchard slope from the Albany and Susquehanna tracks to beg an overnight lodging. Hannah seldom turned anyone away.

"But Hannah!" Nelson protested when he came home late one night from a G.A.R. meeting and spotted still another stranger in the other room. "Hannah, not another tramp! I won't allow you to do this; it's too dangerous!"

"Hush! He might hear you," Hannah said softly. "I couldn't send him away; it was cold; and you weren't here for supper, so I had more than enough food."

And, as always, Nelson softened, for he could not bring himself to deny his wife such small pleasures as her kindliness brought her. Like most of the poor farmers' wives around Tunnel, Hannah worked terribly hard for long hours each day. Gradually the strain had begun to show in her pale face, and her black hair now had some suggestion of gray.

"Did anything happen at the meeting tonight?" she asked her husband.

"Some of the men at supper tonight got to talking about that Indian doctor I mentioned to you the other day. The man's name is Snyder, Dr. Snyder. He lives six miles the other side of town."

"What did they say about him?" Hannah asked.

"Well, my dear," said Nelson, "I don't know whether there's any truth to it, but —"

Hannah looked up suddenly. "Why, you're thinking

about Robbie. Do you honestly — what can this doctor do? Have you talked to people who have been to him?" Hannah nervously pushed back a wisp of hair.

"Well, the Millers have heard good reports of him. Ralph said he cured old Arthur's arm, and Manning Carper's boy went to him about his leg. I don't know whether there's anything to it, but it strikes me it's worth a try."

The Spencers agreed, and the next morning, as soon as the others were off to school, Nelson brought the sleigh around front; Robbie and Hannah climbed aboard; and the three of them started down the road, headed for Dr. Snyder's.

The doctor, who was only part Indian, lived out at the edge of the woods a few miles out of town. No one knew very much about the man's medical background. It was said that he made medicines from the leaves, roots, and herbs he gathered in the woods.

It took the Spencers some time to find a cabin which answered the description Martin Fuller had given Nelson. When at last they found it, no one answered their knocks.

"Let me have a look inside," said Nelson.

He opened the door gingerly, and stepped into a damp, dark, one-room cabin. It had the strong pungent odor of the drying leaves and roots which hung from racks on both sides of the fire. On shelves in one corner of the room Nelson could just make out what looked like a few instruments. A crude bunk with a fur rug thrown over it stood against one wall.

Nelson came out gratefully into the daylight and fresh air.

"Mother, do you really think Dr. Snyder can make my arm well again?" Robbie asked in a little voice.

"I don't know, Robbie. I honestly don't know," said Hannah. "We hope he can."

The Spencers decided to wait, since they had come such a long way.

After what seemed a very long wait to the impatient trio in the sleigh, a tall, ruddy-faced man came from the woods behind the cabin.

"How do you do?" he said courteously. To Robbie, who had expected the "Indian doctor" to be dressed in chieftain's feathers, the man was disappointing, but Hannah was impressed by his fine bearing and the alert look in his dark eyes.

"You must be Dr. Snyder," said Nelson, jumping down from the sleigh.

"Yes, I am," said the man. "What can I do for you?"

"It's the boy, Doctor," said Nelson. "My wife and I wondered if you'd have a look at his arm."

The doctor watched Robbie as he climbed down awkwardly from the sleigh, careful of his stiff arm.

Nelson explained the situation as they followed the tall doctor into his cabin.

They talked for some time before the fire, and the doctor examined the sick arm, but did not say what he thought. After a while, Hannah began to fidget, wondering why the doctor did not show any signs of doing anything about Robbie.

At last, Dr. Snyder rose and went to the shelves where he kept his instruments. He took some leaves and what looked like tough paper torn from flour sacks. From these he concocted plasters which he began to punch full of holes, using a shoemaker's awl. He wrapped them carefully around the boy's arm, and asked Nelson to bring Robbie back in a week.

The first application of plasters was followed by others, each a week apart. When, after a month, there were still no signs of improvement at the end, Dr. Snyder tried another treatment, this time rubbing dogwood leaves against Robbie's arm. But these sessions proved no more helpful than the first. There were fewer and fewer visits to Dr. Snyder's cabin, and finally even Hannah gave up hope. The treatments were given up, and the Spencers found themselves with a very disheartened little boy on their hands.

Life on the farm soon returned to its old monotonous course; Hannah read to him as he lay under the stove in the kitchen, he spent hours of brooding in his attic room, took occasional walks down the familiar slope to watch a train or two pass by. The pattern seldom varied.

"What, O Lord, would you have me do for him?" Hannah asked over and over again in her simple prayers.

There were times, of course, when Robbie did go off the farm. He went to church as regularly as he could. Occasionally, he even accompanied his parents on errands to the neighbors. One night, for example, he was allowed to stay up quite late to accompany his mother on a visit she wanted to make to a sick neighbor. The pair left the Spencer farmhouse sometime after dark, taking the short cut down the slope to the railroad tracks, over the fence, then on down the tracks. Robbie carried the lantern for Hannah, enjoying the way the light danced on the ties as he swung it back and forth.

They stayed longer than they had expected; it was after midnight before they started for home.

"You were tired before we left," he said to her as they made their way up the tracks towards home. "Why did you do it?"

"Because our Lord expects us to," she said.

"Expects us to go out late at night?"

"Yes."

"Even when you're tired?"

Robbie and his mother continued on silently along the track, up the slope again, and back to their own warm, welcoming farmhouse. That conversation was to be remembered longer than either of them knew.

On another evening, Robbie accompanied his father when he made one of his trips to the local cheese factory with milk from the farm. It has been a long day for Nelson. He had worked late that day; it was already dark when they started out.

On the way home they were suprised by a thunderstorm. As they were going down a hill a strap on the harness broke, and they had to stop. Nelson lifted the boy down from the wagon, took the lantern from the dashboard, and gave it to Robbie to hold while he went to work fixing the strap.

"Hold the light, Robbie, so you can see," he said, "and then I'll be able to see."

Holding the lantern was not much to do, but Robbie felt that he was helping his father as he seldom was able to do, and he was to remember this occasion, too, with gratitude.

CHAPTER III

A Surgeon's Knife and an Overcoat

It was in the early spring of 1891 that Cousin Margaret Waite came up from Binghamton for one of her infrequent visits to the Spencer farm. Nelson and Robbie met her at the station in the old democrat, an uncovered wagon with two seats. They spotted her standing on the steps of the coach as the train pulled in. Dressed in her city finery, Margaret was an attractive figure and Robbie and Nelson welcomed her warmly. Guests in the Spencer household, other than the tramps who appeared regularly at the door, were rare indeed.

When they turned in at the Spencers' gate, Hannah was at the door to greet them.

"How wonderful of you to come see us!" said Hannah as Margaret rushed up the steps.

"How wonderful of you to have me!" said their city cousin. "It has been too long. Now, let me look at you. Hannah, I believe you're ten pounds lighter than when I saw you the last time, summer before last."

"A few pounds perhaps," said Hannah, leading the way back into the house. "I've been under the weather the last few weeks — I suppose the boys told you. I had a stomach upset, and I haven't been able to throw it off. But I feel better just for seeing you."

"Now, Hannah," said Margaret with concern at her

cousin's wan face, "you don't have to put on company manners for me, you know. Remember I'm family. What you probably need is to get off your feet and have a real rest. You just let me take over the house for a few days. What's an old cousin for?"

"But, Margaret —"

"Don't you 'But Margaret' me," said the visitor, smiling. "Robbie will tell me where things are, and I'm sure we'll manage beautifully."

There were a few good-natured protests from Hannah. At last she gave in, for she truly did not feel well. Margaret was as good as her word: she cleaned the house every day with Robbie's limited help, cooked meals for the family, helped Nelson with occasional light chores, and — best of all — cheered up the sick patient, Hannah, who seemed hungry for news of other members of the family and this rare chance for feminine talk and hours of reminiscence.

Several times during her visit, Margaret brought up the subject of Robbie's condition, and each time Hannah seemed evasive about it.

Finally, the day before she was to leave, Margaret brought her some milk. It was then that Hannah brought up the subject herself. "Had you noticed any improvement in Robbie's condition? You hadn't seen him for over a year."

"No," said Margaret, "frankly, he seems just about the same to me."

"The doctor tells us his right arm is now about an inch shorter than his left."

"Hannah," said Margaret, "you worry a lot about Robbie, don't you?"

"Oh, Margaret, you have no idea how I lie awake nights wondering what's to become of the boy! Our doctors have tried just about everything they know. It's been a terrible disappointment to us all. In fact, Nelson and I can hardly bear even to discuss it any more. If anything should happen to me —" Her eyes filled with tears.

Margaret embraced her. "Hannah dear, don't worry. Maybe there's something more we could do."

"It's no use," Hannah sobbed. "I know it's no use."

"What makes you so sure? Maybe we could do something for him in Binghamton."

Hannah raised her head and looked into her cousin's eyes.

"Let me take the boy back to Binghamton with me," Margaret urged her. "I know several of the doctors on the medical board. I'm sure they'd be willing to see the boy, maybe even arrange some sort of consultation. Oh, Hannah, it's worth a try. Some of our doctors have been to Europe and have seen what's going on in the clinics in Germany and Austria. There's a Dr. Martindale, who's been abroad. There's Dr. Barstow, who helped Jane's little girl. And there's Dr. Charles A. Ward. People tell me he's up on all the latest developments in medicine. Oh, Hannah, isn't it worth trying?"

Hannah straightened herself up in bed and dried her eyes. "Let me talk to the boy's father," she said, and that evening it was decided that Margaret would take Robbie to Binghamton and try to arrange a consultation.

The next morning, right after an early breakfast, Margaret and Robbie, self-conscious in a Sunday outfit he pretended he had not outgrown, took off for Binghamton.

A forbidding-looking group of bearded doctors gathered at Dr. Martindale's office the following Wednesday. All five doctors were dressed in frock coats, striped trousers, and patent-leather shoes. These men were sitting in a semicircle as Robbie timidly entered the room, removed the shirt which he had just hung about his shoulders, and took the chair Dr. Martindale indicated.

The somber physicians eyed their anemic subject with studied detachment. Except for an occasional question, few remarks were made directly to Robbie. Only Dr. Ward made the slightest effort to put the frightened boy at his ease.

Each doctor in turn would rise from his chair, examine the bad arm, make some comment about the exposed bone, rattle off a few Latin phrases, then sit down again.

"The humerus is exposed, as you can see," said Dr. Drake finally, after the others had had their say. "There's a lot of necrosis there."

"I shouldn't be surprised if we found hospital gangrene in the wound," said Dr. Barstow, walking over to the boy again.

"Hospital gangrene?" said Dr. Martindale. "Hardly, if he's lasted seven years in this condition."

"You've had the benefit of watching some of the Austrian authorities dealing with osteomyelitis, Dr. Martindale," said Dr. Ward after some moments. "What do you think should be done? All of us seem agreed about the severity of the boy's condition."

"I say amputate," he said gravely.

"Don't you feel there is another way out?" asked Dr. Ward.

Dr. Martindale shook his head.

"I'm inclined to agree. I feel amputation is necessary," said Dr. Barstow. "What do you think, Dr. Kusar?"

"I think we should amputate up at the shoulder."

"Gentlemen," said Dr. Ward. "I respect your opinion. There are, I dare say, no finer medical authorities in Central New York than we have in this room right now, and yet I must confess I cannot go along with you on this boy's case. I feel there's a chance — oh, I'll admit it's a slim one — that the arm can be saved."

Robbie had begun to feel faint during this exchange. In all their talk of amputation, the doctors seemed to give little or no thought to how the patient might react to their verdict. He followed Dr. Ward's words intently.

"But what do you propose to do?" asked Dr. Martindale.

"I myself don't propose to do a thing," said Dr. Ward. "But I think there is a chance of saving the arm through surgery."

"There is a chance all right," said Martindale testily — "a chance of losing the boy altogether if you try any of your dainty surgery on the humerus. Mark my words: You're playing with fire. If we amputate, there's hope. At least we'll know then what we're doing. If you try your surgery, you are practically inviting hospital gangrene. Chances are, he'd be —" The doctor stopped short. He looked at Robbie.

"How do you feel about it, son?" Dr. Ward interrupted in a low voice.

"I don't want to lose my arm. I'm scared. I don't understand what you are all saying. But please, please don't amputate!"

A long heated discussion followed. Dr. Martindale and

the others held tenaciously to the idea that amputation was the only answer. Dr. Ward still said he felt it was not. Robbie begged to have Dr. Ward perform the operation he proposed. Cousin Margaret was sent for. She sided with Dr. Ward and Robbie. A grueling half hour more of debate followed. Finally, it was agreed that Robbie, with his cousin's permission, was to be put into Dr. Ward's hands. It was understood that no operation could be performed, however, by Dr. Ward or anyone else until the boy's parents were consulted and written permission given.

"This is in your hands," Dr. Martindale said soberly as they all left.

It took fully a week for Margaret's letter to reach the Spencers and for Nelson to make arrangements to get down to Binghamton. Hannah was still ill. Nelson had to arrange to have friends come in and take over the farm. Someone had to be there just to keep an eye on Hannah. By the end of the week, Robbie had become quite upset despite the efforts of both Margaret and Dr. Ward to keep him calm and confident about his forthcoming ordeal.

When at last his father arrived, Robbie burst into tears. Between having been so long confined to a wearisome routine on the farm, and knowing that his mother was not well, and wondering which of the strange doctors was right, his tension had been mounting. The sight of his father's face unleashed that tension in a storm of weeping. Nelson, himself under a strain at home, did not realize until he put his arms around his son how much he, too, had needed Robbie.

The following day, the arrangements were made; at

Robbie's insistence, Nelson signed a written agreement permitting Dr. Ward to perform the operation. They agreed to meet at the doctor's house the following morning at eight o'clock; the operation would be performed there.

Robbie slept fitfully and was the first one up the next morning. Margaret heard him in the kitchen and came down as soon as she could get dressed. Nelson arrived from the hotel at seven. They were at Dr. Ward's office by quarter of eight. A young medical student of Dr. Ward's, Alex Farwell, met them at the door.

"You must be the Spencers," he said. "We are expecting you."

Alex Farwell was dressed in a soiled white operating frock. There were dried bloodstains on the coat, and one of his surgical needles thrust into his lapel. He showed Margaret to a bare, white waiting room with a very high ceiling, four chairs, and an uncomfortable couch, where she was to wait.

Robbie and his father followed Mr. Farrell down the hall to the back part of the house where Dr. Ward had his office and "operating room."

Dr. Ward greeted them as they entered his office and then proceeded to explain in as nontechnical language as he could just what he was about to do.

"I am going to open that arm, remove all the dead bone I can from the area, then pack the arm for proper drainage, and speed you on your way," said he.

"You make it sound mighty simple," said Robbie's father.

"Doctor, will it hurt terribly?" Robbie asked timidly.

"Robbie, I'm going to try to make it as easy for you as

I can. I will do this in two ways: I shall give you a little of that cocaine some surgeons now find helps a bit. Then I shall work just as fast as I possibly can."

"Robbie," his father said, "you're quite a young man now. I know you'll be brave. If you don't scream, I promise to buy you — an overcoat."

In a few minutes Robbie was on the operating table. The crude cocaine was of little help. He could feel, all too well, Dr. Ward's cruel knife come down into the injured arm. He bit his lip fiercely. Farwell could see the expression of excruciating pain on the boy's face. Robbie tried to turn his mind to the thought of the overcoat his father promised if he would just not scream. He was determined not to give in, but it wasn't easy. Tears streamed from his eyes and perspiration from his half-exposed body.

Dr. Ward made the long incision, then spread the wound wide to give himself access to the bone and to assure proper drainage of the arm.

"O God, help me, help me!" Robbie gasped over and over again.

Dr. Ward, fighting time in order to spare the boy further pain and the risk of gangrene, worked with brutal speed. He cut away a saucerlike section of necrotic bone from the humerus. He wanted to remove all the dead bone he could find. Robbie was losing considerable blood, but by working at phenomenal speed, Dr. Ward finished the operation in just under thirty minutes, then began packing the wound in such a way that it would still drain properly as it began the slow process of healing. Late that same day, Alex Farwell and Nelson were able to take Robbie to the Waites' family home. There they gave him opiates to enable him to get some needed sleep.

For a few days, Nelson waited restlessly to get the doctor's word on whether the operation had been successful. Finally it came: "Mr. Spencer, we have saved it. Robbie will be able to have almost normal use of the arm."

It is not easy to describe the great joy and sense of reprieve which filled the Spencer house in the weeks which followed. Robbie did not return home for two months, but in the meantime the good news had already done much to keep Hannah going.

"It is as though a dark storm cloud was lifted at last," she wrote Cousin Margaret. "We had been living under that cloud for seven years. Somehow, I never realized fully how constant and dark a shadow it cast on our lives, until it was taken away. I find myself saying over and over again, 'My baby is well again.'"

Hannah did her best to make Robbie's home-coming as perfect as she could. She did not want the boy to know how ill she had been. She forced herself to get up and cook the home-coming dinner, which included hash, Robbie's favorite dish, and rich poundcake. After dinner, Nelson brought out the promised overcoat.

"It's yours, my boy," he said tenderly. "It's all yours, because you were man enough not to scream."

Robbie's eyes filled with tears. He could not speak.

Hannah went over and kissed him. "Saint Paul would have told you, 'Robbie, my boy, you have indeed fought a good fight.'"

For all its seeming gaiety, Robbie's homecoming marked the close of a chapter for the boy. It marked the end of seven years of suffering for him; it also marked the beginning of Hannah's last month. For the "upset stomach," which months before had seemed superficial, soon became critical, and Dr. Harvey Beardsley admitted himself no match for an incurable condition. Late one evening, the doctor came from Hannah's bedside to tell the Spencers that her heart had gone to rest.

CHAPTER IV

Cheese-making at Tunnel

EDITH KINGSLEY WAS SITTING in front of the fire, her feet up on a little stool, working on the squares for a small child's quilt. Her baby was due any time now.

"Charles," she said in a weary voice, "I sometimes pity the elephants. They have to wait such a long, long time for *their* babies."

"Oh, Edith," said her husband, "I know it's been a long ordeal for you, but you're coming down the home stretch. Doc Beardsley told you the baby wasn't due till the twentieth and here it is only the nineteenth."

"Yes, I know," she sighed. "I shouldn't complain. We're lucky to be having a family at all."

"And we're lucky to have a house like this! It's big enough for a raft of children," said Charles. "Besides, we own it outright — not like those poor devils who have to carry heavy mortgages and make those pestiferous payments every month, whether crops are good or not."

Edith measured the quilt square on which she was working.

"I think mortgages are the invention of the devil, I do," said Charles.

"I don't," said Edith. "Lots of people around here could never live if they didn't have a mortgage."

"I suppose so. All the same, I'm glad we're free and

clear on this place. Look at what happened to Nelson."

"Do you think that was just a case of a heavy mortgage?" Edith asked, threading another needle. "It strikes me that the poor man just went to pieces over Hannah's death."

"Robbie tells me he's much better since he took the job working down on the farm in North Colesville."

"Still, it's a shame, Nelson working on somebody else's place. It doesn't seem right," said Edith.

"Robbie told me that Irving likes his job at the Endicott Shoe Company," Charles said as he lit his pipe.

"And where's Guy, now that Nettie's living in Binghamton?" Edith asked.

"He's working in a railroad construction gang, Robbie tells me. Apparently, he doesn't like it much," said her husband.

"I can't exactly say that I blame him."

Charles Kingsley, who owned the local cheese factory, was a kind of celebrity as far as the citizens of Tunnel went. He and Edith lived in a spacious old house — a house with large rooms and high ceilings, furnished with oversized golden oak furniture. Weather permitting, Charles spent most of his off-duty time gardening. Edith shared her husband's interest — more, it was said, because it kept him home than because she was herself a rose garden enthusiast.

When Nelson Spencer gave up fighting the upkeep of a hillside farm and a heavy mortgage, he moved to North Colesville and left Robbie on his own. Robbie stayed for a while with neighbors. Then, partly out of pity, Charles hired the boy to go to work for him in the cheese factory. He and Robbie agreed to the businesslike, if not generous, terms of fifty dollars for six months plus room and board.

To Robbie, with only the one bundle of belongings, any offer of shelter sounded wonderful, but particularly one coming from the Kingsleys, whom he had known since he was a little boy. Edith had been a good friend of Hannah's and had often gone out of her way to be kind to the boy whenever he was around.

But he was not around much now. Robbie's workday began at four in the morning after a quick breakfast of bread and milk. He had to rush over to the factory, start the fire for the engine, and take in the milk as the early farmers began to arrive. All day long, he helped Mr. Kingsley make cheese. Then, after Charles had left for the day, Robbie had to stay around until about nine o'clock when the last farmers came in with their milk.

Robbie had only been on the job two weeks as a trainee the morning Edith had her baby.

"Robbie, it's happened! The baby's come!" Charles shouted as he rushed in the door. "Edith had a boy, just about twenty minutes ago!"

"How wonderful! Is she all right?" Robbie asked.

"All right? He's wonderful!"

"I mean Mrs. Kingsley."

"Oh, she's fine, just fine," said Charles. He stopped pacing the stone floor. "Robbie, I'm taking off today. I won't be in. You've been here two weeks. You know how to take over —"

"But, sir!" Robbie protested.

"Don't worry, Robbie, you can make cheese — I've taught you how to do it." He rushed out, slamming the door behind him.

At first, Robbie was almost paralyzed with fright. Would he remember what to do? Had he really been paying enough attention those two weeks?

There was only one way to find out, he decided.

The milk was already in the vats. He first heated it to the proper temperature, added the rennet to make it coagulate, and then drew off the whey and allowed the curd to go down into the vats.

"But what next?" he asked himself, after the first rush of confidence.

Then he remembered. He recalled watching Charles next cut the mixture up into squares and put a mill over it that looked like a coffee grinder. Robbie fed the squares of curd into the mill and ground it up into small particles.

As he worked, more and more the next steps came back to him: he remembered about the press, the cheesecloth, the squeezing of the whey out of the cheese, the job of putting the mixture on conveyers to allow it to cure.

"I'm proud of you, very proud of you, Robbie," Charles said when he returned late that afternoon, although "relieved" would have described his feelings more accurately. "Robbie, you really did it! You made as fine a batch of cheese as I could have. If you keep it up, mark my words you'll be a real cheese maker someday."

"Do you really think I could?" Robbie asked, proud at the praise despite his exhaustion.

"Think you could? I *know* you could. Look at what you did today, after only two weeks here!"

In the months which followed Robbie worked hard at the factory. He was frail, of course, and still very young-looking. Sometimes, this look of youthfulness bothered the boy. He wanted so much to seem grown-up to the farmers who came to the plant that at one point he started rinsing his mouth out with a little "borrowed" whiskey when he saw farmers drive up in their wagons. He would then rush out and say with all the breathiness he could muster, "H-h-how are you?" — until finally one old man leaned over the side of his wagon and whispered, "Robbie, don't you honestly think you're hittin' the bottle a little too hard?"

Robbie worked his long days at the factory, learning what he could, but the strain became too much for him. At the end of six months, he reluctantly told Mr. Kingsley that he was leaving.

"But I don't understand," Charles said. "I've had great plans for you. Why, if you stick at this thing, you could easily be making eighty dollars a month someday as a cheese maker."

Robbie said, "I know, Mr. Kingsley, and I certainly appreciate all you have done for me. But I'm not too strong. My right arm is getting stronger all the time, but it has been bothering me a lot lately. I honestly feel I'm not up to the work."

"But, Robbie, I had begun to look on you as —"

"I'm sorry to have to give up the work, Mr. Kingsley," said Robbie.

"But what do you plan to do?"

"You know that the people we rented our farm to moved out last week. Well, Guy's quit the railroad gang. He's gone back and plans to farm the place. He's married now, you know. He and Carrie — that's my sister-in-law — they've asked me to go live with them."

"But you can't do *farm* work!" said Charles. "You're not up to it, my boy."

"I'm not going to," Robbie explained. "You know how I've always loved trains. Well, Will Monroe down at the depot said he'd take me on as a kind of station helper, and Will Cole, the telegraph operator, told me he'd try to teach me to be an operator."

"So you're going to be an apprentice to Will Cole! That's really wonderful, Robbie," said Charles. "Folks tell me he's the best operator between here and Albany. You know, good operators get as much as thirty-five dollars a month. Will they pay you while you're learning?"

"No, they can't — they're not allowed to. I'm too young."

"I guess that's not too much of a problem at first," said Charles, "seeing as how you'll be living with Guy and all. Well, Robbie, I wish you the best of everything. I hope you'll drop around to the factory once in a while. I'll miss you, you know. I got used to having you around."

That evening, right after work, Robbie packed his things, said good-by to the Kingsleys, and headed out of town, along the old familiar road he had been too busy to travel for some weeks. He thought the countryside more beautiful than ever.

Guy met him at the door. "I was watching for you, Robbie boy," he said. "Seems sort of natural to see you come up the path."

Robbie grasped Guy's hand, and for a moment he could not speak.

CHAPTER V

Signalman's Helper

THE SCAR ON HIS ARM looked like the gnarled trunk of a tree, but Robbie assured Guy it felt stronger all the time. Just now, however, with his poor arm and what little schooling his mother had given him, Robbie felt that there were few jobs around Tunnel he could handle. The railroad, he told his brother, fascinated him most. He longed to be a brakeman, but Mr. Monroe and the boys at the station told him he was too young. Somewhat reluctantly, he had taken on the job of telegraph operator's apprentice and general station helper.

"There's no pay in it," Robbie warned his brother, "but there's no tuition fee either. I'll be earning my lessons doing chores around the depot."

Early the next morning, Robbie left the house, ran down the slope, climbed over the railroad fence, then hurried on into town through the tunnel. As he approached the depot, he spotted Mr. Monroe, standing in the door looking at his monstrous pocket watch.

"He's clocking me, I'll bet," Robbie told himself as he began to run.

The 7:28 was standing in the station. The engineer was inside with Will Cole, picking up a few messages.

"Welcome to the service of the Albany and Susquehanna!" said Mr. Monroe jovially. "Tunnel may be a mighty small speck on the map, my boy, but a powerful lot of freight rolls through here, and it's our job to see that it keeps on rolling."

To Robbie, Mr. Monroe, in his blue-and-gold station agent's uniform, looked as much a hero as Admiral Nelson.

"Will's inside," said Mr. Monroe. "He's expecting you."

Robbie went through the little waiting room into the telegraph office.

"Be with you in a minute, Robbie," said Will. He was tapping out a message. In a moment he stopped, spun around in his revolving chair, and said to the engineer who was standing beside the desk, "McKibbee, this is Robbie Spencer, my new assistant. Robbie, meet Mr. McKibbee. He's engineer of that 7:28 standing out in the yard."

Robbie shook McKibbee's hand, then drew his chair closer to Will.

"I just wired the dispatcher in Albany that McKibbee was here," Will explained. "Now we're waiting for word that the train can go ahead."

Just then the message began to come through. Will wrote down on his pad: "MC KIBBEE WEST WILL PROCEED ON YOUR RIGHT.

"Now watch this," said Will. "I have to repeat this same message back to Albany, word for word."

Will tapped out the message again and signed it with the Tunnel station letters UN. In about two minutes, back came word from the Albany dispatcher: OKAY — SAB.

"SAB are Ralph Gosmer's code letters," Will explained. "Whenever a message comes through signed SAB, that means Mr. Gosmer is on duty as dispatcher."

"Golly, Will," said Robbie, impressed.

"This may take you a little time to catch on to," Will said sympathetically. "But it's easy once you get the hang of it."

In the months that followed, Robbie worked hard around the depot; each morning he swept the place, carried out the ashes, and built a fresh fire in the stove. Sometimes, he gave Mr. Monroe a hand with a switch out in the yard.

In exchange for this work Will Cole, the daytime operator, and Doc Beardsley's daughter Clara, who went on duty in the evening, gave Robbie lessons in Morse code and railroad terminology.

When he was not working in the telegraph office or helping Mr. Monroe around the yard, Robbie liked to hop aboard a train. He was very sure-footed and liked nothing better than to walk along the top of a drag of freight cars, swaying back and forth. He got so he could keep his balance from one end of a moving train to the other. Sometimes he would ride home through the tunnel. Several times, he got on an express by mistake and instead of being able to get off at the foot of the farm he was carried all the way to Binghamton.

Only a single track passed through Tunnel, and it was the job of Will Cole and the others to see that the track was kept free. There were no signals, of course. When a train stopped to pick up extra freight, one or two men would drop off the train some distance behind and clamp a torpedo to the rail. Another train coming along behind ran over the torpedo. The sound of the explosion was the signal for the second engineer to slow down.

One afternoon, while walking down the track near the

switch house, Robbie spotted a torpedo on the track which had not yet exploded. Just for fun, he picked up a heavy coupling pin and threw it at the torpedo. He hit it all right. The torpedo exploded with a bang, and a sharp piece of tin flew at Robbie and cut him rather severely over the eye.

Robbie looked sheepish as he walked into the station a few minutes later with his vest tied around his forehead.

Mr. Monroe, who had heard the explosion, guessed what had happened.

"Robbie," he said, "this will teach you that torpedoes were made only to warn engineers. Better go home and have that 'tended to."

For some time, Robbie continued as a telegraph operator's apprentice and station helper. In that time he mastered the Morse Code and learned much about railroading, but — as well he knew — he was still far from becoming the kind of skilled operator the telegraph schools turned out those days. Guy noticed how discouraged Robbie had become over his chances of getting ahead with the railroad.

Robbie had been much excited a few months before when the railroad had put in a telegraph substation at the foot of the Spencers' slope.

"Maybe I'll get to be the new operator," he had said to Guy hopefully.

He was transferred to East End, as the new station was called — but not as head operator. Will Cole made no bones about that. Robbie was still just an apprentice. That evening, Robbie went home in great discouragement. He ate dinner without saying a word.

One afternoon, when the East End operator had run

up to the Spencer house for a minute or two, a message started to come in. Robbie wrote it down as fast as he could: WHEN DID FORTY-FOUR CLEAR THE YARD?

Robbie opened the door, called to his colleague to hurry back. No response. Finally, in desperation he did what he was never supposed to do without the supervision of his superior: he sent a message. FORTY-FOUR HAS NOT YET ARRIVED, he wired, signing himself proudly RS. Five minutes later another message came through: THEN FORTY-FOUR MUST HAVE GONE AROUND ROBIN HOOD'S BARN, BECAUSE IT HAS BEEN REPORTED IN DOWN THE LINE. Later that evening, the Albany Dispatcher wired Tunnel: KEEP THAT HAM OFF WHO SIGNS HIMSELF RS.

As winter came around again and Robbie still had no apparent hope of landing a paying job with the railroad, he quit. For several weeks he moped around the farm. Sometimes he went into town. On several occasions he managed to pick up a little money doing odd jobs for Charles Kingsley or the Monroes or pinch-hitting at Mr. Miller's General Store. But, as Robbie told his brother, he felt a strange urgency to leave Tunnel.

"Leave Tunnel?" Guy asked. "But what good would that do?"

"I have a curious feeling lately that I'm supposed to leave," said Robbie.

"What good would that do, Robbie?" Guy asked. "Wherever you went, you'd run up against the same problems you've had here. You can't do hard physical work, because you're not strong enough. You can't tackle desk work, because you haven't the schooling."

"Guy," Robbie said slowly, "I've been doing a lot of thinking. I'm certainly no help to you around here."

"Robbie, we want you to feel you have a place to stay," said Guy.

"You've been wonderful to me," said Robbie. "I know that. But lately, Guy, I've had a strange feeling I ought to go into the ministry."

"The ministry!" Guy exclaimed.

"Yes, the ministry. Oh, I know. I'll have to start my schooling from the very beginning. I know that; and at sixteen that won't be easy."

"But Robbie!" Guy was still a little stunned. "The *ministry!* Oh, sure, you were always the Bible reader around here. You got that from Mother. And you've been a great brooder up in the attic room of yours. I guess that was natural, with you sick and all. But the ministry! I just never —"

"I know it's hard to understand, Guy," Robbie said. "It may sound conceited, but please don't take it that way. I've just had a strong feeling lately that God spared me and healed my arm for a reason. And I think maybe that reason was the ministry."

"Only you can judge a call like that," said Guy. "What do you propose to do?"

"I thought I'd hop a train for Albany and go see the Bishop there. Maybe he knows a school where I could work my way through."

Nelson Spencer came to Tunnel for the day the following Sunday, and Guy told him of Robbie's plans. He said nothing.

Later in the afternoon when a few neighbors stopped by to see Nelson, he told them, "Robbie thinks he wants to study for the ministry."

Robbie looked at his father, aghast. Had Guy told him?

"Yes, Robbie wants to become a preacher," he said, not looking in his son's direction, "and I am not one to put my hand forth and touch the ark of the Lord."

So it was all right. He did not object. Robbie was overjoyed. His father said nothing more on the subject, but he stood for a long time at the door, looking at his boy, before he took off for North Colesville, and said "God bless you" when he went.

A few nights later, on Christmas Eve, Robbie put on his heavy overcoat, which was badly worn now at the sleeves, said good-by to Guy and his wife, and took off for the depot in town.

"I'm off for Albany," he said to Clara Beardsley, who was on duty at the station when he arrived. He put his lantern down in a corner and walked over to the warm stove.

"Going up there for Christmas?" Clara asked.

Christmas? The thought had not occurred to him.

"No, Clara," said he. "I'm going up to see a man there about going to school and studying for the ministry."

"The ministry!" said Clara. "Robbie, I'd never thought of it for you, but you know, it makes sense. I think you'd be a good pastor."

At least Clara believed in his plan. They talked for some time. Finally, Robbie said good-by, went out the door and across the yard to the freight train which was standing there. He climbed up into the cab of the engine.

"Why, Robbie Spencer!" McKibbee exclaimed in surprise. "Are you going to give me some company to Albany?"

"Yes, if you don't mind," Robbie said.

"Mind? Why I'm delighted," said the tall engineer. "It's a month since I've set eyes on you. What have you been up to? Will Cole tells me you've quit the railroad."

In a few minutes Clara came to the station door with word from the dispatcher to proceed. McKibbee gave a shout, and they started on their way.

The next morning, the freight train pulled into the Albany yards in a blinding snowstorm. Robbie hopped down from the cab, then tramped through the snow to the station to scrub up. He could not get all the grime off, but he did the best he could.

"Golly, but I could do with a haircut!" he exclaimed when he caught sight of his wild mop of black hair in the glass. "But I guess it's too late now."

He grabbed a quick sandwich, then walked over to where the Bishop lived and up the long drive to the palatial home.

Robbie rang the bell on the wide paneled door. In a moment a little boy appeared.

"Is Bishop Doane at home?" Robbie asked timidly.

The boy turned. "Grandpa!" he shouted. "There's someone here to see you."

Robbie heard a muffled groan from the next door. In a minute, Bishop William Crosswell Doane came around the corner, his gold-rimmed spectacles swinging from a purple ribbon. He wore the gaiters and apron of a British bishop. Robbie's heart pounded as he saw his stern face.

"I'm Robert Spencer from Tunnel, New York," he said haltingly.

"Yes, yes, what is it?" said the Bishop.

"I'm here to see about studying for the ministry," he continued. "I haven't had any schooling, Bishop, but I thought maybe you —"

"Where did you say you were from?" asked the Bishop.

"Tunnel, sir."

"Where is Tunnel?"

"Broome County, sixteen miles from Binghamton, sir," said Robbie.

"Broome County?" said the Bishop. "Then you're not in my diocese. You're in Bishop Huntington's diocese. He is the man for you to see."

"But, Bishop —" Robbie said.

"Besides, this is Christmas morning," said Bishop Doane. "It's nine-thirty now, and I have a sermon to preach at the Cathedral at eleven. I am still working on my sermon, and so I'm afraid I shall have to ask you to leave. I'm terribly sorry. I do wish you well. Good day to you."

He shook Robbie's hand and showed him to the door. It swung to with a heavy click and Robbie Spencer walked dejectedly down the drive through the snow.

CHAPTER VI

Help at Port Crane

MONTHS WENT BY. Back in Tunnel, Robert made no plans to go see Bishop Huntington. Discouraged by the brusque rejection in Albany, he contented himself with doing odd jobs around town. Each morning, he helped Guy milk the cows, then headed off for whatever light work he could line up on the nearby farms.

One afternoon, while picking apples over at the Monroes', Robbie happened to mention to Dave Marsh, a schoolteacher who was helping him, about his thoughts of entering the ministry. Dave seemed genuinely interested, and Robbie told him at length about the disappointing trip to Albany the winter before.

"Robbie," said Dave finally, "if you're still serious, I think I know someone who could help you. He's the Methodist preacher over at Port Crane — his name's Guy Snowden. He and his mother, Sarah, are great friends of mine. I know Guy could help. I don't know anything about schools, but he does. He's a graduate of Johns Hopkins and Drew Seminary."

"But what good would that do me?" asked Robbie. "I'm seventeen now, and I'm nowhere near ready for a place like Johns Hopkins. I know I've got to start my schooling all over from the beginning."

"No, don't get me wrong," said Dave. "I just mean that

Guy Snowden is an educated man. He's been around. He knows a good deal about different schools. I'm sure he's one man who could help you get into school somewhere."

"And line up a job, so that I can work my way through?" Robbie asked.

"Yes, I'm sure of it," said Dave. "At least it's worth a try, isn't it? I'll be glad to give you a letter of introduction to Guy, if that will make you feel any better."

Robbie agreed. After all, it was not a great trip over to Port Crane, the last whistle stop before Binghamton. Late that evening, Robbie went around to Dave's room at Mrs. Porter's to pick up the letter of introduction. The next morning, dressed in his Sunday best and wearing his father's old Prince Albert, Robbie climbed aboard the short freight train which was standing on the orchard siding. Before long, the train began to move slowly onto the main track, and Robbie was on his way to Port Crane and the Snowdens'.

That afternoon, he knocked at the Snowdens' door.

"Would you see who it is, Mother?" asked a voice from the study.

"It's some melancholy young man dressed in black," said Sarah Snowden, peeking through the front curtains.

Guy Snowden entered the room. His mother was still peering out the window.

"Guy," she continued, "just look at him. He has a mane of black hair that would do honor to an anarchist!"

Guy laughed and walked out to the door. "Do come in," he said smiling.

"Are you Dr. Snowden?" Robbie asked, feeling very ill-at-ease in his father's oversized Prince Albert.

"Yes, and your name?" asked the young minister cordially.

"Robbie Spencer — Robert Nelson Spencer, that is," was the reply. "I'm from Tunnel. Dave Marsh sent me." He handed Dr. Snowden the wrinkled letter of introduction.

"May I take your coat, Mr. Spencer?" said Dr. Snowden, noticing the young man's discomfiture.

"Thank you," said Robbie, obviously much relieved to be free of it.

"And this is my mother," said the minister. "Mother, this is Mr. Spencer from Tunnel. He's a friend of Dave Marsh."

Mrs. Snowden greeted him warmly, as her son had, and any misgivings Robbie may have had about receiving from Dr. Snowden the kind of reception he had received from Bishop Doane were quickly dismissed.

Dr. Snowden showed Robbie into the study, and his mother went to the kitchen to prepare tea. Robbie had never seen such a room. Books up to the ceiling lined all four walls. Sermon notes and open reference books cluttered the front of the roll-top desk.

Sarah Snowden could tell that Robbie and her son were going to hit it off famously — they talked incessantly. At tea they spoke of James Fenimore Cooper's books, of Tunnel and Port Crane and Dave Marsh. The young minister questioned Robbie closely and sympathetically. Dr. Snowden had a gift for drawing people out. Robbie sensed the man's genuine interest and told him in detail about his early years in Tunnel, the accident, the suffering which followed. He told him about Dr. Ward and the operation and how his mother had lived just long enough to see him cured. He spoke of the cheese factory and his work with the railroad.

Then Robbie told him about his decision to enter the ministry, how suddenly he had made his decision, and how disheartening his trip to Albany had been.

"You can hardly blame the man," said Dr. Snowden. "Christmas Day is a pretty busy day for a bishop, you know, even without young callers from Tunnell!"

He then talked to Robbie at length about the ministry and about the long, rigorous training ahead of him. He painted as honest and bleak a picture of what Robbie faced as he could. Finally, he was convinced that Robbie did have his heart set on the undertaking, no matter how great the obstacles.

"My problem is to get into school," said Robbie, "some school that will be willing to start me all over again and let me work my way through."

Dr. Snowden paced the floor silently for a few minutes.

"I have it!" he said finally. "We shall write Dr. Levi S. Sprague. He's President of the Wyoming Seminary at Kingston, Pennsylvania. He's an old friend of mine. You write him a letter, stating your problem, and I'll enclose a covering note with it."

"Do you think there's a chance?" Robbie asked.

"You won't know if you don't write to him," said the minister. "Let me clear a place here for you at the desk."

Robbie sat down at the desk and wrote his letter to Dr. Sprague:

DEAR DR. SPRAGUE,

I am writing you at the suggestion of the Reverend Guy Snowden. I am seventeen. I have had practically no education, because my right arm was badly hurt in an accident when I was seven.

I am afraid I do not have money enough for tuition, but I hope you can give me a job to do that will help me work my way through.

I hope someday to become a clergyman. I hope you will look favorably on this letter.

Dr. Snowden hopes so, too.

Respectfully yours,
ROBERT NELSON SPENCER

Dr. Snowden wrote a covering letter in which he explained in detail all he knew about Robbie and urged Dr. Sprague to do what he could to help.

The two letters apparently had their effect. Robbie was still a guest at the Port Crane parsonage when the postman arrived with a letter from Kingston.

"It's from Wyoming Seminary," Robbie exclaimed, "from Dr. Sprague! He says, 'Come on. We have a place for you and a job as well. . . .' Oh, Dr. Snowden! How can I ever thank you and your mother for what you have done!"

Robbie read and reread the letter with its handsome red seal and the motto *The True, the Beautiful, and the Good* across the top. "I'm on my way at last!" he said to himself exultantly.

That afternoon, he left for Tunnel to pack up for school.

Before he went, he reiterated his thanks to Guy and his mother.

"How can I ever thank you for all you have done for me?" he said again.

"That's enough of such talk," said Sarah Snowden, cheerfully.

"Do you still think he looks like a melancholy anarchist, Mother?" Guy asked.

"Hush, Guy!" said Sarah, smiling sheepishly. "Robbie,

I have a strange feeling about you," she said, turning to him eagerly. "I have a hunch you've come into our lives to stay. I have a curious feeling you will always be a friend." She kissed Robbie's cheek, and in a moment he had gone.

CHAPTER VII

"The True, the Beautiful, and the Good"

THE AUTUMN SUNLIGHT was streaming across the wide lawns of the seminary campus as the carriage rounded the corner. They approached the school, and Robbie saw the impressive buildings for the first time — historic Swetland Hall; the Nelson Memorial Hall, which had been completed only a few years before. Robbie told himself that it was even more wonderful than Dr. Snowden had said.

The driver leaned over the side of the carriage to speak to a student who was walking along the path. "Pardon me, son," he said, "but could you tell us where we might find Dr. Sprague?"

"Over at Centenary Hall," said the student, pointing toward a large building down the road. "Chances are you'll find both Dr. and Mrs. Sprague there. I think I just saw them go in the door."

Wyoming Seminary had been founded in 1844 by the Oneida Annual Conference of the Methodist Episcopal Church, Guy had told Robbie, and through its first half-century had already established an enviable reputation as a coeducational school which not only gave boys excellent preparation for college but also gave girls that training in the humanities which characterized the good "finishing school" course of the period.

The carriage pulled up in front of Centenary Hall; Robbie hopped down. The driver handed him his pack, wished him well, then took off down the drive. Robbie stood there a minute, just looking about him at the campus. The trees were beginning to turn in the clear air. It looked just as Robbie imagined college would be, and already he felt a stirring of proud loyalty to his school.

Robbie cautiously pushed open the great door. As he stepped into the hall, he saw Dr. and Mrs. Sprague there, evidently discussing the repainting of the walls.

"Why, how do you do?" said Mrs. Sprague with surprise.

Robbie was a bit stunned at running right into the Spragues this way. He stared at them for a moment — Mrs. Sprague was tall and slender, well dressed, with her hair parted in the middle and framed in a neat braid; President Levi L. Sprague was a spare man with a high forehead, a well-trimmed goatee, and searching eyes behind rimless glasses.

"You must be Guy Snowden's friend," said Dr. Sprague, understanding Robbie's plight. "Welcome to Wyoming, Robert."

Guy Snowden had warned Robbie that he would find Dr. Sprague a little brusque perhaps, but that he was not to be afraid of him. Instead, Robbie found the man most cordial.

"We've been expecting you," said the President's wife, holding out her hand to him.

They stood talking for a few moments. Then Dr. Sprague draped his coat around his shoulders and led the way across the campus to the room which had been

assigned to Robert. As they entered the dormitory and
started up the stairs, Dr. Sprague asked him about his
family.

"My father's name was Nelson, too," he said, in a
friendly, natural way.

When they reached the room, Dr. Sprague tried the
window himself to make sure it was not stuck.

"Later on," he said, "you will be told about your job
— you are going to be the assistant janitor in one of the
dormitories."

"Oh, that's fine," said Robert, much relieved that Dr.
Sprague had not forgotten about the promised job.

Dr. Sprague sat down to talk with Robbie for a while.
"You may find it a bit rough going at first," he warned
him. "That's to be expected. After all, you have had virtually no schooling, and we have had to put you in the
primary department. It may not be too easy a situation,
for a seventeen-year-old like yourself. The other students
may give you a bit of a ribbing at first. But don't let it get
your goat. From what Guy Snowden tells me about you,
I'm sure we needn't worry — I am sure you will be a good
soldier, and make out beautifully."

He stood up and surveyed the room carefully again.
"Well, Robert," he said, stroking his beard, "I must be off.
I don't think you'll have any trouble finding the dining
hall. All you have to do is follow the crowd when you
hear the bell." He gave Robbie a quick smile and left.

In the months which followed, Robert attended each
morning as many of the primary classes as Dr. Sprague
felt he could absorb "without getting mental indigestion":
English grammar under methodical Professor Wolfe, elo-

cution taught by understanding Adelia Breakstone, penmanship under bespectacled Professor Dean of the Department of Business. It was not easy taking arithmetic, spelling, and the other primary courses with ten-year-olds, but, as Robert wrote to Guy Snowden, he had resolved to make a go of this at all costs.

"Work hard, Robert," red-bearded Professor Thurston had said to him the first week he had Robbie at his table in the refectory. "I know it's a bit hard, but you wouldn't think of training for a race by walking slowly around the track, would you? Of course not. Here, have some more potatoes."

Each morning, Robert attended his classes; then each afternoon, when the other students went out for athletics, Robert went to his job in the dormitory. This consisted of carrying two huge iron buckets through the halls and emptying the slops from each room into them. When the buckets were empty, he could carry them without too much difficulty, but as he filled the buckets with slop it was all he could do to bear the weight. In fact, the first few days he worked in the dorm, he thought he would never make it down that last hall, so great was the strain on his weak arm.

But he knew he must not give in. This job was not like the job at the cheese factory. Either he could take it, or school and his hopes for the ministry were out. When he finished his work the first afternoon, he flopped down on his bed half-sick with fatigue. "But I made it!" he told himself over and over again. "With God's help, I'll make it again tomorrow." And he did. As time went on, he found that the work became easier and his arm all the stronger for the exercise.

Guy Snowden came by, one Saturday, en route to a clergy conference nearby.

"How's school going?" he asked Robbie.

"As well as can be expected, I suppose," replied Robbie with a shrug. "They're throwing it at me pretty fast, you know. I'm really carrying quite a schedule."

"But they're only doing that to bring you along as fast as you're able to go, you know," said Guy. "Dr. Sprague says you are not the world's greatest mathematician, but he tells me he's really quite pleased with the way your English is coming along. Professor Wolfe told him —"

"Oh, I like Professor Wolfe so much!" said Robert. "He's the one teacher whose classes really keep me interested through the whole period."

"Well, he told Dr. Sprague that he thought you had a real flair for words," said Guy. "Mother and I have been noticing that lately in your letters, too."

The two friends walked down the path. "Tell me, Robert — I notice they frown on calling you 'Robbie' — tell me, Robert, are you happy?" Guy asked. "I know it's not been easy going to classes with ten-year-olds."

"No, it was hard at first," said Robert. "They made fun of me; but everyone's more used to me by now, I guess."

"I notice you had four demerits for instigating a hall rush one Sunday night," said Guy, teasingly.

Robert only smiled, without explaining. He himself wasn't sure he understood the reason for that escapade.

"Have you met any girls you like?" Guy asked.

"A few."

"Anyone special?"

"I suppose you might say one — her name's Beatrice Kipp. She lives over there at Swetland," said Robert.

"We've danced a few times at school dances. But she'd never look at a boy like me."

"Why on earth not?"

"I haven't anything to offer," said Robert, with some heat. "I'm poor, just an assistant janitor with a crippled arm."

"It's not like you to whine, Robert," said Guy gently.

"Oh, I know — you're right. It's just that she'd never look at me twice — she has so many admirers. She's rather interested in one, too, I know. Besides, she's leaving school the end of next semester."

"You seem pretty stoical about it all," said Guy.

"Oh, I admire her all right, but I look upon her as someone far away, as unobtainable as a star."

Guy laughed. "But you've not really answered my question, Robert. *Are* you happy? How do you feel about the ministry after all these weeks here?"

"I love it here," said Robert. "People have been wonderful to me — like the Spragues, Mrs. Thurston, Professor Wolfe, and the boys in our dorm."

"But what about the ministry?" Guy asked again.

Robert stopped and looked at Guy. "I've never been so sure of anything in my life. Getting away from home, coming here to school, getting a chance to think about it all — it's just convinced me that I'm meant to go into the ministry."

"What do you mean 'meant to'? That sounds a little proud to me," said Guy.

"Oh, heavens, I don't mean it to sound that way," said Robert. "I just mean I have a constant feeling that somehow our Lord meant me to suffer all those years — that

He wanted to test me, and then spared me to go to work for Him."

"But everyone should serve Him — laymen as well as clergy," said Guy.

"Yes, yes, I know," said Robert; "but I feel that I'm drawn to the ministry in a special way, and I feel that I have no other course but to go that way. It may be rough for me — it hasn't been easy so far. But somehow, if I try, He'll see that I end up in the ministry if it's where I really belong. It's actually in His hands."

At the end of the afternoon, Guy had to leave. "I must be going," he said. "God bless you, Robert. And, oh — I almost forgot — Mother told me to give you her love."

CHAPTER VIII

A Close Call at Wilkes-Barre

AT THE END OF HIS FIRST YEAR at Wyoming, just when Robert appeared to be making real progress at school, it happened. All one January night, Robert was up violently sick at his stomach. When morning came, he forced himself to go down to breakfast, but he took one look at the food and headed right back to his room.

"What's wrong, Robert?" asked Professor Thurston, who came up a few minutes later to check on him. "Sick to your stomach?"

"I was up all night, sir. I had chills and an upset stomach and I ache all over."

The professor felt the boy's forehead.

Later that day, the school doctor, Dr. Cross, came over to see Robert. He examined the boy carefully — his eyes, ears, nose. He felt Robert's warm forehead and took his pulse. He held down the boy's tongue with a spoon handle and examined the inflamed throat.

"A little Fleet's Phosphate should fix you up in no time," said the doctor finally.

During the day and the night that followed, Robert's fever continued to rise. By morning he was delirious. President Sprague sent for Dr. Cross again.

"What do you think it is?" asked Dr. Sprague when the physician came down from Robert's room.

"Levi," Dr. Cross said sternly, "I may be completely wrong, but we can't take chances. We've got to get the boy out of here at once."

"What is it?" asked Dr. Sprague.

"I may be wrong, but I think it's — typhoid fever."

"Good Lord, no!" exclaimed Dr. Sprague, clapping a hand to his forehead. "Good Lord, if this ever spread!" he went on, horrified. "We must get him away from here at once. We can try Wilkes-Barre first."

"The city hospital? I'm sure we could get him into the Charity Ward all right," said Dr. Cross.

"Poor devil! He's really wretched, isn't he?" said Dr. Sprague.

"His fever's much worse. Right now, he's out of his head."

Dr. Woodbridge Johnson stood, looking pensively out his office window at the snow falling on the street in front of the hospital.

"He's been here a week now, Doctor," said the nurse, "and there's still no improvement. If anything, he seems worse." She watched the doctor. He showed no reaction to her words. "His fever seems to be on a kind of high plateau," she added.

Dr. Johnson turned and smiled at her. "You're pretty concerned about him, aren't you?"

Miss Richter flushed. "Oh, I don't allow myself to get disturbed about patients," she said, looking away.

"I don't blame you," said the doctor. "After what Sprague told us about the boy and what he's been going through this week, I don't blame you. He's a likable chap. I'd like to see him pull through, too. I want to make certain we give him all the care he needs."

"There are eighteen others in the ward with him, Doctor," said the nurse.

"See that there's at least one nurse nearby at all times. I'll authorize it, if necessary."

Dr. Johnson sat down at his desk and began to look at some reports.

"What do you think of the boy's temperature?" asked the nurse, with a kind of desperate insistence.

"It's all part of the typhoid pattern. The temperature keeps rising until it hits a plateau. Then it often stays there for a couple of weeks."

"A couple of weeks!" Miss Richter exclaimed.

"Sometimes more."

"And you say we still can't feed him?"

"No," said the doctor. "We might run the risk of intestinal rupture, if we did."

"But he's had nothing but milk since he's been here."

"I know that," said Dr. Johnson, "but he's in no condition to eat."

"Is there anything I should be doing to try to bring down the temperature?"

"There's nothing much you can do," said the doctor. "The boys tried lifting him into the ice tub, didn't they?"

"Yes, several times," she said, "but maybe they didn't do it right. They filled the tub with cold water and put big chunks of ice in it. Then they lifted the boy on a taut sheet and put him in the tub."

"That was right," said the doctor. "It didn't help bring the temperature down for long, did it?"

"No, I'm afraid nothing we do helps very much," Miss Richter said in a despondent voice. "I have a hunch we may lose him." The doctor said nothing. Miss Richter picked up her notebook and pencil. "I'd better be getting back to the ward," she said.

Two tedious weeks of fever passed before suddenly Robert's temperature showed a pronounced change. The doctor was elated. A few hours later, however, the temperature started to climb again, and Robert began to thrash about in delirium. The nurse sent for Dr. Johnson.

In a moment, he appeared. He tried to quiet the boy and take his pulse. There was that curious double beating again. He felt Robert's forehead — it was very warm.

"He said something about his ears hurting him, before," said the nurse.

"Let's have a look." The doctor leaned over his patient, the nurses watching him anxiously.

"See the swelling?" said Dr. Johnson softly. "He has it back of both ears. Notice how red it is?"

The doctor continued to examine the swollen areas behind both ears.

"Miss Richter, would you please find Dr. Feld and ask him to come here as soon as he can?" he said finally.

A half-hour later, Dr. Feld arrived, examined Robert carefully, then confirmed Dr. Johnson's diagnosis of mastoiditis.

"We must operate as soon as possible," Dr. Feld said. "I don't like the looks of this at all. With his weight down so, all he's got is a fifty-fifty chance, if that."

"I know it's a gamble," Dr. Johnson said soberly, "but there's nothing else we can do."

"What's this nasty scar on his right arm?" asked Dr. Feld.

"A childhood sled accident — hematoma, osteomyelitis. Some man up in Binghamton did a saucerization on the humerus."

"Good Lord, he took out quite a bit of it!" said Dr. Feld.

Back in Dr. Johnson's office, they discussed plans for the operation. Dr. Johnson sat down at the desk and took out some paper. Dr. Feld flopped down in a chair, pulled a small bottle of whisky out of his coat pocket and offered it to Dr. Johnson. "Here, have some!"

"Better go easy on the bottle!" his colleague said.

"I won't be operating for a few hours yet," said Dr. Feld. "Besides, I can't work without a little, just to calm me down and steady my hand."

Dr. Feld took a swig. Dr. Johnson shook his head.

"Oh, Wood, stop being so goddam righteous!" he barked.

"We've got to get word to the school," said Dr. Johnson. "What about family?"

"I don't know for sure. I'll check with Dr. Sprague."

He wrote a brief note to Dr. Sprague, describing the urgency of the situation, and the danger.

During the night, Dr. and Mrs. Sprague and Dr. Cross drove to Wilkes-Barre. They arrived just in time to meet Dr. Feld before he went into the operating room.

"Did you smell his breath!" exclaimed Mrs. Sprague. "I think it's a disgrace, any doctor going about with liquor on his breath. Why —"

"They say he's very good," said Dr. Sprague, hastily.

Just then Dr. Johnson appeared.

"My, but I'm glad you're here!" he said, shaking Dr. Sprague's hand.

"How's Robert's condition?" asked Dr. Cross.

"About the same, Doctor."

"What do they do in an operation of this kind?" President Sprague asked.

"They make an incision back of the ear, enter the bone to get at the cavity of the mastoid, and let the pus out," Dr. Johnson explained.

Mrs. Sprague fanned herself with her gloves.

"You see, it's actually a kind of osteomyelitis," said the Doctor. "It's somewhat comparable to the condition he had in his arm."

"Will he have much of a scar?" asked Mrs. Sprague.

"Probably, since some of the bone must be removed and the wound kept open and draining. Often it leaves a rather large twisted scar."

"They'll remove a little of the packing at a time," Dr. Cross added, "as the wound begins to heal."

"Does that hurt much?" asked Mrs. Sprague.

The two doctors glanced at each other.

"Our job right now is to save a life, Mrs. Sprague," said Dr. Johnson. "Will you excuse me?"

As soon as Dr. Johnson's first urgent message had arrived, President Sprague had dashed off two notes — one to Robert's oldest brother, Irving, who was visiting Guy Spencer in Tunnel, the other to Dr. Snowden, who had just moved to Moscow, Pennsylvania.

When Irving read his letter, the news came as a terrible shock. "I've got to go see him at once," he said.

"I'll go with you," said Guy Spencer.

"No, Guy. There's no use our both going. He's probably too sick to see anyone anyway. You'd best stay here with Carrie. But do get word to Father as soon as you can. Poor Robbie, he's had more than his share of tough luck, it seems to me."

When the Reverend Guy Snowden told his mother the news about Robbie, and that there was a chance he might not live, her eyes filled with tears. "Oh, Guy, it's not fair! It's not fair."

"Mother, I'm going to Wilkes-Barre."

"Of course — you must," she said, and went to pack his bag.

The next morning, two men entered City Hospital at the same time and walked to the desk — one, a tall man in his middle thirties in a worn gray coat and hunting cap; the other, a young clergyman in black.

Irving was the first to ask for "Robert N. Spencer in the Charity Ward."

Guy Snowden looked startled. "You, too? I'm Guy Snowden. I've just come down from Moscow. Dr. Sprague wrote to me about Robbie. . . . You must be Irving," added Guy. "Robert has told me about you."

"I've heard a lot about you, too, and how wonderful you were about getting him into school."

The man at the desk had disappeared. He came back in a few minutes with Miss Richter.

"These gentlemen are here to see Mr. Spencer," said he.

"Do sit down," said the nurse.

Irving introduced Dr. Snowden and himself.

"Robert came out of the operation nicely," said Miss Richter. "The doctor says he's sure he's going to be all right."

"Can we see him?" asked Guy. "His brother's come all the way from upstate New York."

"Yes, both of you may see him, but only for a minute. He's still a very sick boy." Miss Richter led the way up the stairs.

"I warn you, his looks will be a bit of a shock," she said. "His head is heavily bandaged, and the poor boy has lost a lot of weight. We haven't dared feed him solid food. He's down to around ninety pounds, I'm afraid."

"Please," Irving insisted, when they reached the ward, "you go in first. I'll wait here in the hall."

Irving waited. Guy returned in a few minutes. He could not speak.

"You may see your brother now, Mr. Spencer," said the nurse.

Irving followed her down the aisle to the bed where his brother lay motionless. As Irving stood there, looking down at the limp, emaciated boy, Robert opened his eyes. They looked grayer than ever, under the wide white bandage.

"Irving!" said Robert smiling wanly. "Irving!"

Irving burst into tears. "Oh, Robbie! Robbie!" he sobbed, seizing his brother's hand. "You're going to live! You're going to be all right!"

CHAPTER IX

Moscow

When Robert was dismissed from the hospital the last week in April, Guy Snowden came down to take him back to Moscow.

"There's to be no argument," said Guy. "It's all decided. Mother insists on your coming to us."

"But, Guy, I can't —"

"Listen here, Robert. The doctor says you've got to rest, and our climate is as good a one as you'll find anywhere. Come on — let's not argue. The carriage is out front."

"But honestly, Guy, I'm not strong enough to do anything around the house or earn my board."

"Forget it," said the minister. "You'll get stronger very soon. Then you can give us a hand around the place. I've got four churches on Sundays, you know. I can't handle all four every week. You can help me with that."

"I'd like that," said Robert.

"It will give you a taste of what a minister's life is like."

"Do you think I'll be up to it soon?" asked Robert. "What did the doctor say?"

"Robert, there's no hurry," said Guy. "The important thing is for you to get rest, food, and a little fat on your bones."

"I'm heavier than I was a month ago."

"And Mother will fatten you up in no time," said Guy.

Then he added, smiling: "Know something? It may do us Methodists some good, having an Episcopalian like you around the place!"

Robert laughed. "You know what they say: If we could get the fire of Methodism under the water of the Baptists, we might get enough steam to run the Episcopal Church!"

That spring and early summer, Sarah Snowden did all she could to nurse Robert back to health. Guy smiled to see his mother put her cakes and pies on the table in the months which followed. His mother was really determined to fatten up their boarder!

At first, Robert was allowed to do very little. Sarah insisted upon waiting on him hand and foot. She even brought him snacks between meals. Meanwhile, between parish calls, services, and meetings of one sort or another, Guy was being kept very busy.

"I'm happy as a clam at high tide," Robert told Guy. "Why, I'm having a wonderful time poring over all your books and having long talks with that brilliant mother of yours. Besides, I'm feeling stronger all the time."

By late summer, Robert was not only well enough to help Mrs. Snowden around the house but was now able to trim the bushes and mow the lawn as well. Occasionally, Guy asked him to make a few parish calls. "It'll give you a little taste of the pastoral ministry," he told the boy.

In September Robert began to accompany Guy on his rounds to the different churches every Sunday.

"How about your reading the Scripture Lesson this morning?" Guy asked one Sunday as they approached Daleville.

Sarah sat in the back of the chapel that morning and watched Robert as he nervously stood up to read the lesson. His voice sounded deep and strong. He read with simple directness:

"For I am persuaded, that neither death, nor life, nor angels, nor principalities, nor powers, nor things present, nor things to come, nor height, nor depth, nor any other creature, shall be able to separate us from the love of God, which is in Christ Jesus our Lord."

Later that day, when she and Guy were alone, Sarah told her son, "When Robbie read that lesson today, it was almost as though I had never heard those words before."

"Yes, I know," said Guy. "There is a powerful force there. You can tell that he believes right down to the soles of his feet. Did you see him with the children afterward? They loved his clowning."

Early the next morning, without giving any reason, Guy went up to Scranton and did not return till late that night. Sarah had gone to bed, but Robert was still up — partly out of curiosity and partly because he was engrossed in reading.

"Robert?" Guy asked as he entered the front door. "I'm glad you stayed up. I have some exciting news for you."

"What news could you possibly have for me?" Robert asked, rubbing his eyes.

"Well, I didn't tell you this, but I've been corresponding for some weeks with the School of the Lackawanna — that's a fine school in Scranton."

"Yes, I know. I've heard of the place."

Guy sat down in his favorite chair. "A lot of wealthy railroad and coal men send their sons there, you know," he said, putting his feet up on a footstool. "Well, Robert, I spent the morning out at the school with Dr. McCann, the headmaster, and he's agreed to take you on, starting with the fall semester."

"But what about tuition, Guy?"

"I'm coming to that. I explained your whole case to him, and he's prepared to take you on as a day student on a special low tuition basis."

"But, Guy, how will I —"

"I'm prepared to help you with your tuition, for one thing. And Dr. McCann was most generous. But in exchange for this, I'll expect you to help me a little more with my churches on Sunday and do the lawn and other chores around here other times when you're off."

"Would I be a day student? Where would I live?"

"That's all set, too. After I talked with Dr. McCann, I had lunch with a Mr. Halstead. He's an official of the railroad. I wanted to talk to him anyway about a rural book-lending service he's interested in sponsoring. Well, in the course of the conversation we got to talking about railroads, and I told him some of your experiences with the Albany and Susquehanna."

"What are you leading up to? Am I going to live at the Halsteads'?"

"Better yet, Robert," said Guy. "You're going to live right here and commute. Mr. Halstead asked all about you. I told him about your bout with typhoid and how kind Dr. McCann had been that morning about your tuition. Finally, he said to me, 'Guy, I want to help the boy, too. I'm going to get him a free pass on the railroad, so that he can commute back and forth every day.' And after lunch, we went back to his office and he had his agent fill out the forms for it then and there."

Robert beamed. "Guy, I can hardly believe it — when do I begin?" he asked eagerly.

"The twenty-second of this month."

"Oh, wonderful!" said Robert eagerly. He looked at his friend shrewdly. "Why did you really have lunch with Mr. Halstead?"

"Why do you ask?"

"Did you really want to discuss the book-lending service — or did you plan all along to try to get me a pass?"

Guy smiled sheepishly. "Do you know it's after midnight?" he asked, getting out of his chair. "Time for bed," he said. The two young men smiled at each other with a brotherly tenderness.

The winter passed quickly for Robert in commuting to Scranton every day, studying every evening, and doing odd jobs around the house and yard on week ends. On Sunday, he regularly helped Guy by taking services at one of the chapels and even doing a little preaching.

"You should hear him sometimes," Guy told Dr. McCann at the school one day. "There's good solid Bible teaching in his sermons, a little poetry, sometimes even humor."

The following spring, Sarah Snowden wrote to Dr. Sprague about Robert's progress, and about how happy he seemed, though he was still attending classes with boys half his age, and how his health and spirits had recovered.

During the summer months Robert got a job selling stereopticon slides door-to-door in the rolling countryside of Northeast Pennsylvania and in his own native Central New York. As the fall of the third year approached, Robert applied, at Guy Snowden's urging, for admission to Dickinson Preparatory School, an on-campus adjunct to Dickinson College in Carlisle. Robert was accepted. Several weeks later, taking with him his clothes and books, his summer earnings and the Snowdens' promise of further "tuition help," Robert said good-by to Moscow and set out for unpredictable years in yet another strange town.

CHAPTER X

Dickinson College

ROBERT, A LANKY TWENTY-ONE-YEAR-OLD, arrived in Carlisle late on a September afternoon in 1898, and asked for directions at the station.

"You can't miss the place," the station agent said. "Tall building it is — too tall if you ask me. There's a long flight of steps up to the front door, and they've got one of those cupolas on the roof. Oh, you won't have any trouble finding the school."

Dickinson Preparatory School, Robert had learned, was founded in 1783 as a preparatory school for the college; it had been discontinued in 1869, and reopened in 1877. Although it was not technically a part of the college, the school was under the immediate supervision of the President and Executive Committee of Dickinson College. Since almost all the teachers at the school were members of the college faculty, seniors did not have to take entrance exams for Dickinson. As the catalogue explained: *Students passing satisfactorily on the studies required for admission to the freshman class will be received without further examination.*

Not long after he left the station, Robert found himself standing at the front of the steps leading up to the South College building. The front door opened, and a young man appeared.

"Won't you come in?" he said.

Robert picked up his bag and ran up the steps.

"I'm Professor Heckman," said the young teacher, holding out his hand.

"My name is Robert Nelson Horatio Spencer," the newcomer explained as they entered the hall.

Heckman smiled. "Where are you from, Bob?"

"I guess you'd say I was from North Colesville, New York. At least that's where my father works."

Robert followed Mr. Heckman into a room at the right, where they sat down. The professor told Robert at length about the school, what courses he would be taking and what books he would need.

Finally, he led the way to Robert's room.

"You've been assigned to Room Number 13," said the Professor. "You're not superstitious, are you, Bob?"

"No, sir, I'm not," Robert said with a grin.

"Good. I think you'll find the rooms comfortable. They've just put steam heat in all of them." He showed Robert his room, then turned to leave. "Oh, yes, I almost forgot — supper is at 6:30. I'll see you then."

That evening, two of the students whom Robert met at supper took him on a short tour of the campus.

One of them, Tom, pointed out West College, where President James Buchanan had once lived.

"Did he go to Dickinson?" Robert asked.

"He sure did. He wasn't much of a student, though, from what they say."

Later, Robert returned to his room, and unpacked the clothes and books he had brought with him, and prepared to settle in.

Parents are urged not to furnish or permit others to

furnish their sons with an undue amount of money, he read sleepily in the catalogue. *If experience teaches anything, it is that students are thus demoralized.*

"Small chance of that!" Robert said as he put out the lamp beside his bed and drew up his covers.

In the following months, Robert had to make many new adjustments, but this time, better prepared than he had been for Wyoming Seminary or Lackawanna, he slipped into the new routine "with happy ease," as Principal Fred Downes described in his faculty report on the new boys.

Robert found the work hard. He had to spend long hours over his history texts especially. The languages, particularly English, however, were beginning to come easier for him, but mathematics was still a stumbling block. Fred Downes gave Robert extra help with that subject. Teachers supervised the study-hall periods closely and made a point of giving the boys individual help wherever it was needed. Try as he would Robert found figures very hard to handle. He even wrote a poem on the subject called "Aftermath."

> If, in a crucible, I held
>   The nether god's most with'ring wrath,
> With hardened heart and steady hand,
>   I'd pour the contents out on Math.

But Robert was beginning to strike up many new real friendships. A number of his classmates came as he did from farm families, and like himself, many planned to enter the freshman class at Dickinson College the following fall, so he and his friends had much in common.

College rules forbade on-campus athletics, but Robert went out for a number of sports at nearby Dickinson Field.

"We had a series of elaborate tests one day," Robert wrote his father. "They wanted to test our strength. Well, I'm afraid I made no records — I was thirty-first out of a group of forty-five. With the kind of exercise we're getting now, I think I can do better another time, though."

One evening, a group of students from the college made a special visit to his room.

"Why, come in!" said Robert with surprise, when he saw them at his door.

When Mr. Heckman heard voices and laughter coming from Robert's room a little later, he came down the hall to find out what was going on. The undergraduates were just leaving as he appeared.

Mr. Heckman looked in on Robert, who announced excitedly, "Mr. Heckman — I've just pledged to Beta Theta Pi!"

"Congratulations, Bob," said the professor. "Beta is a fine house."

"The best!" Robert insisted. "You know, Mr. Heckman, this is one of the nicest things that have ever happened to me."

Mr. Heckman had never seen his student look more confident or happy.

Regularly on Sundays, Robert earned a little extra money conducting services at rural missions. "Spencer preached at Newport (Pa.) last Sunday morning and evening," said the *Dickinsonian,* a weekly.

On campus, too, Robert began to make quite a name for himself as a speaker, and that spring he competed for the Reed Prize in Oratory with "Daniel Webster's Address at a New England Murder Trial."

"Gentlemen," he recited with all the resonance of a seasoned senator, "it is a most extraordinary case. In some respects it has not a parallel anywhere, certainly not in our New England history. . . ."

Robert won the prize and with it the warm friendship of President Reed. One spring afternoon the President asked Robert to come to his office.

George Edward Reed, meticulously dressed in black with a gray ascot, was seated at his broad desk. "I am pleased at the reports I have had of your work, Robert," he said. "Apparently, you have been doing very well. The faculty have recommended that you be admitted to the freshman class next fall as a special student."

"How wonderful!" Robert exclaimed. "You have no idea what this means to me."

"I can well imagine, son," said Dr. Reed. "But actually I called you in for quite another reason. I think I have a summer job for you. My friend Major Pilcher has been given the responsibility of supervising the cataloguing of the state law library in Harrisburg. He needs extra help this summer and has agreed to take on a few of our Dickinson boys."

"But I've had no experience for that kind of work, sir," Robert said.

"No matter, Bob — you'll have help. You boys can live here at the college and commute to Harrisburg daily during the summer."

Any misgivings Robert may have had about the job disappeared the morning he met tall, graying Miss Fell from the Drexel Institute, who had come over from Philadelphia to help direct Major Pilcher's staff.

"I haven't any experience," said Robert at once.

"That won't matter," Miss Fell said, reassuringly. "You're going to have that desk over there, right opposite my office, aren't you?" she asked. "I'll always leave the door open, so that you will feel free to ask as many questions as you like. If someone brings you a book and you don't know where it belongs, Bob, don't say anything," she said. "Just wait till the person leaves, then ask me. I'll be glad to tell you how it's classified."

"I'm sure I can learn," said Robert. "You're very kind."

"Of course you can," she said, "and now we had better get started."

Like the other freshmen who entered the college direct from Dickinson Prep, Robert did not have the adjustment which boys new to the campus had to face that next fall. In fact, he sometimes acted among his new classmates as though he half owned the place, until, that is, some upperclassman came along to remind him of his freshman status.

But Robert and a number of the freshman ringleaders had their revenge on the upperclassmen. Instead of holding the class banquet in town, where men from the other classes were sure to find and heckle them, Robert and a few of the others rounded up the class for a special secret meeting. One day after that, they completely disappeared from campus. It was only later that the upperclassmen learned that they had all taken a train to Chambersburg and had their banquet there.

Finally, at the end of a Hell Week which included much paddling of the pledges, Initiation Night did come and with it the longed-for pin, the explanation of the grip, the end of the heckling, and what many of the boys declared to be the greatest Beta Banquet ever.

Later that same evening, when the Betas were still whooping it up over at the Wellington Hotel, Robert slipped away and took the train for Lancaster, and on Sunday morning, at St. John's Church, Lancaster, Robert was confirmed by the Right Reverend Ethelbert Talbot, Bishop of Central Pennsylvania. At the same service, Robert was also formally admitted by the Bishop as a postulant for holy orders.

In the chancel, at the end of the offertory, Robert repeated the responses to Bishop Talbot's questions.

"You may sit in the choir stalls," the Bishop said to Robert under his breath.

"If it's all right, I'd rather stand," Robert whispered. "It hurts me to sit down — initiation last night, you know."

Bishop Talbot smiled and walked to the sanctuary.

The following summer, the Bishop found work for Robert as a lay reader and assistant at the impressive St. Luke's in Scranton. With their rector away, the two younger priests, Father Houghton and Father Nash, welcomed the help of the young lay reader and at once put him to work reading some of the weekday morning and evening prayer services, helping with parish calls, and doing other assigned work which did not require the services of a clergyman.

"Take good care of the boy, and teach him all you can," said the Bishop. At St. Luke's that summer, Father Nash tutored Robert in Greek and Latin and taught him many "do's" and "don'ts" of visiting the sick. Father Houghton, for his part, spent long hours helping Robert improve his speaking and the reading of the services.

During the hot summer months not many people showed up for the weekday services downtown, but Robert read them faithfully just the same. One humid morning in July only one man showed up in the congregation. When Robert came to the responsive Psalter selection, he read his verse, then waited for the man to chime in with the second.

"I'm sorry, but I can't find my glasses," the man intoned in an unctious churchly way as if his own words were Scripture. "Read your verse, and I'll catch up with you next time round."

Robert read his verse.

Again the churchly voice: "I still cannot find my glasses."

As Robert told Father Houghton later, "It was all I could do to keep from laughing. To hear the man wail about his glasses in that cathedral drone of his, you'd have thought he was the Psalmist himself!"

But life was not all church services, parish calls, and Greek lessons that summer. Robert went to a number of ball games with Father Nash, Saturday outings with other young people from the parish, and several of the summer dances.

That September when Robert was packing his belongings to go back to Dickinson, Father Houghton came to his room.

"Bob," he said, "I want you to know how much we have enjoyed having you here."

"You and Father Nash have been wonderful to me," said Robert, gratefully.

"You have no home to go to, do you?" asked the priest, pacing back and forth. "Your father has no house of his own now, and we'd like to think you're somewhat a part of this house. You will always have a warm welcome here, you know."

"Even at a busy time — like Christmas?" Robert asked.

"Even at a busy time, like Christmas."

They shook hands on it.

Back at Dickinson, Robert found students hotly debating the Philippine question and other major issues of the presidential campaign which had sent William Jennings Bryan out around the countryside, trying to win the White House away from Mr. McKinley. The debates even found their way into the "other-worldly" pages of the *Dickinson Literary Monthly*. Student sentiment ran high over the campaign. Voices frequently became shrill on Saturday nights at the Hotel Wellington whenever the names of Bryan and McKinley were mentioned. Life on campus was anything but the quiet affair suggested by Robert's poem which was published that fall in the *Literary Monthly*:

Processional

The bell that tolls the summer out is done,
And, like unto a chancel, Dickinson,
Comes our processional, bowing low before
Thy shrine of Knowledge and Thy God of Lore.

That fall, Robert's fund of borrowed money began to run very low. Thanks to the Bishop, he got a job taking services on week ends down at Greencastle, some forty-odd miles away.

He spent that Christmas in Scranton. On the way back he wrote another poem which soon appeared in the *Literary Monthly:*

A Watch-Night Etching
Midnight was clamorous with bells
As down and out the Old Year went;
A holy hush, and countless unvoiced
prayers
Welcomed the New in silence eloquent.

One evening, as the weather became warmer, the Betas celebrated some occasion with an elaborate banquet which went on until midnight. When at last the party broke up, Robert and his friend Arch took off for the Wellington Hotel — the one place they knew would still be open — and sat there, chatting and quenching their thirst, for hours. When dawn came, the two Dickinsonians, by this time somewhat less thirsty, decided to leave.

"But we can't go back to the campus now!" Arch exclaimed. "They're sure to have missed us."

"We'd better find a place to hide and sleep it off," said Robert.

"Where could we go?"

Robert thought for a moment. "I know just the place — the cemetery."

"The cemetery!" Arch exclaimed.

"Why, sure," said Robert. "Nobody would ever think of looking for us there. Besides, there's a wonderful stone wall around the place, and we wouldn't be seen by passers-by."

And so, still in their bedraggled evening clothes, they made their way over to the old graveyard and wandered through the gate.

"Lord, but those stones look uncomfortable!" said Arch.
"Better than getting caught, though."

For a few minutes the pair wandered among the graves,
looking for the widest slab they could find. Finally, they
chose the grave of Molly Pitcher, the celebrated heroine
who once traipsed

> O'er Monmouth's field of carnage drear
> With cooling drink and words of cheer . . .

Robert awoke around noon, shook himself, and headed
shakily toward South Hanover Street. It had begun to
drizzle, and Frank Sellers, a fellow Beta, spotted Robert
in his damp, soiled evening clothes, grabbed him by the
arm, and headed him up the street toward the campus.

They had not gone more than a few yards when they
ran into Frank's brother, Montgomery Sellers, a professor
at the College. The professor looked somewhat startled.

Frank hurried Robert past. "Bob, we haven't time to
stop."

Arch, on the other hand, did not awaken until the old
caretaker at the cemetery went in late that afternoon and
got him up.

The next morning, Robert was called in before the
President.

"There are no marks against you, Bob," he said. "This
is a first offense for you, and I know it was just a prank.
But it must not occur again. Arch, I'm afraid, is going
to be expelled from college."

"But, Dr. Reed, I'm just as —"

"Bob, Arch has been in trouble before. We just can't
tolerate this sort of thing over and over again."

Robert went to Arch's room, and threw himself down in a chair angrily. "It isn't fair, Arch," he protested.

"What do you mean it isn't fair?" said Arch. "I deserve to be kicked out. Dr. Reed is right."

"Well, Arch, I guess I won't be far behind you anyway."

"Why do you say that?"

"I'm really down and out now. My money's just about all gone," said Robert. "I had to borrow some to come here in the first place, and now most of that is used up."

"Can't I lend you something?" asked Arch.

"Heavens, no," said Robert. "I need too much. But it's very good of you. Frankly, it looks now as though I'll have to quit school for good this term."

"What'll you do then?" Arch asked.

"Well, I was talking to Canon Ernest Smith in Harrisburg about the possibilities, and he suggested that I go to the Cowley Fathers' Monastery in Boston. They're Episcopal monks," said Robert, "of the Society of St. John the Evangelist, and they're great preachers."

"You weren't thinking of becoming a monk yourself, were you?" Arch asked.

"Oh, Heavens, no," said Robert. "But the Cowley Fathers will always help young men studying for the ministry. Canon Smith has already written them about me. He thinks they could prepare me for theological seminary."

"Well, no matter what happens to us," said Arch, earnestly, "I hope we can somehow always keep in touch."

Robert stood up and put his hand on his good friend's arm.

"I hope so, too," he said, with feeling. Then he smiled,

boyishly. "You know I think I shall always have a peculiar fondness for Molly Pitcher after last night."

Arch smiled too as he pulled his dusty suitcase out from under the bed and prepared to leave.

CHAPTER XI

Cowley House and Cold Nashotah

WHEN ROBERT ARRIVED at Cowley House in Boston, a tall, gaunt old monk named Father Field met him at the door. Robert followed him back to the office of the Superior, Father Osborne, a very large man with penetrating eyes.

"We are always happy to try to help young men prepare for the priesthood," he said smilingly. "May God bless you in that study, Brother Robert."

Father Field then led Robert upstairs to his third-floor room overlooking Bowdoin Street.

"You will be expected to wear a black cassock like the rest of the brothers," said Father Field. "You will also be expected to attend all the appointed services and abide by the rules of the House — for instance, not speaking at meals unless Father Osborne breaks silence. Of course, you may talk in places like the Common Room," Father Field went on, "or when you are with the brothers going over your lessons, or —"

"Father Field!" a voice called out from downstairs.

"Brother Robert, will you excuse me?" he asked, darting away.

Robert closed the door and without thinking turned the key. To his dismay, it broke off in his hand.

A few moments later, there was a knock at the door. "Brother Robert?" a young voice said. "The Father Superior wants you to come to lunch. The others are already eating."

"But I can't get out!" Robert said in embarrassment and explained what had happened.

A few minutes later, Father Field's voice through the door asked, "Why did you lock your door? Whom did you fear? This is a monastery. We never lock doors around here."

"But I didn't mean to lock it," answered Robert. "I didn't think what I was doing — I just did it automatically."

"Well, this is Friday," said Father Field. "It's a fast day anyway; so I guess it's not too bad."

"Can't we find a locksmith?"

"We are poor here, Brother Robert. We cannot afford locksmiths."

"Father Field, just wait a minute, if you will." Robert walked over to the window, looked out, and spotted a narrow ridge stretching along under his window over to the window of the next room. He turned back to the door. "Father Field," he said, "I believe that by holding on to the window ledges and the crack in the masonry of the wall, I can work my way along the ledge outside to the next room and climb in the window."

"No, no," Father Field protested. "No, don't do that — you might be killed. Brother Robert, can you hear me?"

"Yes, I hear you."

"We will get a locksmith at once!"

All that summer Robert read and studied under the learned monks. Most of them were getting on in years. They were all graduates of Oxford, had written books,

and were well-known preachers who had conducted
preaching missions all over the United States. Here,
under their guidance, Robert managed to telescope much
of the required pre-seminary instruction into the space
of a few summer months.

To earn his board, Robert did odd jobs around the
house: ran errands, rang the bell for services. Between
long hours of study, attending the frequent services, and
working at different jobs around the place, he was able
to leave the house only briefly for an occasional walk, and
he treasured these small outings.

One morning he decided he wanted a smoke. Immediately after the early service and before breakfast, Robert
slipped away from the precincts of the house — where no
one dared smoke — and walked as far as the Boston
Common.

Dressed in his cassock, he stood at the entrance to one
of the diagonal walks which go through the Common,
took out a cigar, and lighted it. No sooner had he taken
the first deep puff than he spotted the figure of the Father
Superior approaching, looking singularly large and for-
bidding in his cassock, cloak, and shovel hat.

Robert immediately palmed the cigar, slipped his
hand into his cassock pocket cigar and all, then waited
for the Superior to pass. Instead, Father Osborne paused
beside him.

"Good morning, Brother Robert!" he said amiably.

"Good morning, Father," Robert replied nervously. The
cigar continued to burn.

"And what a glorious morning it is!" said the Superior,
taking a deep breath.

The two men stood for a moment looking out at the

Common. Tramps who had spent the night on the grass were beginning to stir from their pallets of newspapers. Men and women were hurrying to work. Robert's cigar continued to burn.

"Robert," said Father Osborne in a contemplative tone of voice, "our Lord often looked out on scenes like this on the Mount of Olives, people getting up off the ground . . ."

As Father Osborne talked on and on about the scene before them and about the wonders of Boston in general, Robert's cigar grew shorter and hotter until he knew he could stand it no longer.

"Well, Brother Robert, I must be on my way," said Father Osborne at last, "and you will want to finish your smoke. Good day!" With that, he swept back up the street toward breakfast, and Robert stood for a moment stunned as he watched Father Osborne disappear up the street.

During the summer months, both Bishop Talbot and Father Osborne wrote to Nashotah House, a seminary in Wisconsin, about admitting Robert. To enter a seminary a student needed a regular B.A. degree or its equivalent. Robert could claim neither. But on the basis of his work at Dickinson and the "extraordinary amount of work covered at Cowley House," the Warden of Nashotah finally sent word for Robert to come on in the fall as a special student.

That September, headlines rocked the nation with the news of President McKinley's assassination. Theodore Roosevelt became the twenty-sixth President of the United States, and columnists vied with one another in predicting what the dynamic "Teddy" would be like.

The day came for Robert to leave Cowley House and head west to Nashotah.

"You're sure you have enough money?" asked Father Field as he was preparing to go.

"Well, I have at least half a train fare more than I expected," Robert said, "what with this reduction for theological students."

"And what about your meals?"

"Now, just you forget about me," said Robert smiling.

"Forget about you? Brother Robert, we shan't forget about you. You may be sure we will keep you in our prayers for many years to come."

The next day, when Robert arrived at Buffalo to take the Grand Trunk across to Michigan, the agent told him that he could not travel half fare, and explained that divinity students could do so in the United States, but not in Canada, where the government made no such allowances.

The price of the ticket used up all the money Robert had left. All that day and the following night he had no money for food. At Grand Rapids he knew that he had to change cars. When he arrived, he took out his large old railroad watch, a memento of days at Tunnel. There would be just enough time to look up the local bishop before catching the next train for Grand Haven.

Robert rang the doorbell, as Bishop John Newton Mc-Cormack and his family were about to sit down to dinner. Robert followed the Bishop into his study, explained his predicament, showed his credentials, and asked if he might borrow a little money to cover his meals.

"I'll pay you back as soon as I get to Nashotah," he said.

Bishop McCormack stared at the bedraggled intruder. "What are those cords around your shoes?"

"I had to tie something around them, sir," Robert explained nervously. "The soles were coming off. I plan to —"

"Here, Mr. Spencer," the Bishop said. "I'll lend you this —" and he handed him a silver dollar. "But remember," he added sternly, "I expect it back."

Robert just made it to the station in time to jump aboard the already-moving train to Grand Haven.

From Grand Haven, he took the boat to Milwaukee and then went on up to Nashotah House and its six hundred acres of Wisconsin countryside — picturesque, isolated, quite unlike any place he had ever been. Here he began the rigorous seminary training.

He had not been there more than ten days when one morning the Warden, Father Webb, called him into his office.

"I've just had a letter from the Bishop of Western Michigan," he explained. "He tells me that a young man named Robert Spencer, who passed through Grand Rapids enroute to Nashotah, borrowed money from him, with the promise to pay it back at once. It seems the money has not yet arrived, and he has written me to find out about it. Is this true? Did you borrow money from him?"

Robert stared at the floor. "He's quite right, Father Webb. I did go to his house to borrow the money. I was hungry — I hadn't eaten in twenty-four hours. He lent me the money on condition that I'd pay it back as soon as I got here. Unfortunately, my allowance from Bishop Talbot hasn't yet come. I've been expecting it any day."

"Tell me, Spencer, just how much did you borrow from the Bishop?"

"He lent me a dollar, sir."

"A dollar! A dollar!" Father Webb's face grew flushed. He stood up and began to pace the floor.

"Oh, Father Webb, I'll make good on the thing. I'll pay the Bishop."

"All this over a dollar!" Father Webb fumed. He turned to Robert. "Please give this matter no further thought. I shall settle this with the Bishop myself."

Three days later, Robert received a most apologetic letter from Western Michigan. "Whenever you pass through Grand Rapids," Bishop McCormack wrote, "you will be a guest of my house . . ."

The Nashotah campus was beautiful. Robert could see twelve lakes from his window, and he liked nothing better than to take walks around the lakes as a change of pace from long hours of study or time spent in the classroom.

Robert spent a year of rigorous study at Nashotah. He did not find it easy to keep up with classmates with four full years of college behind them. Theology, church history, homiletics — Robert had his first dose of these and other required courses that year. Sundays, he spent in field work: taking services at the rural churches nearby, helping out wherever he was assigned.

More than once, on a Saturday night, Robert and a classmate had to go across frozen snow to the little church in Hartford. On one occasion, the thermometer read as low as 25 below, and the two seminarians had to sit up all night, stoking the fire to get the place warm enough for the congregation on Sunday.

Robert wrote Father Nash: "I'm busier than I ever was at Dickinson, but I am enjoying every bit of it — new friends, stimulating teachers, gorgeous country, interesting field work! I am more than ever before convinced that the priesthood is my calling."

But again his money ran out. At Commencement time, Robert reluctantly told the Warden that he was heading for Kansas to visit relatives, and that he would not be back in the fall.

Junction City, Kansas, hardly sounded like another forward step toward the priesthood, but it was soon to prove itself more of a step toward happiness than a discouraged Robert Spencer seemed to realize as he stoically climbed aboard the train that was to take him there.

CHAPTER XII

The British-born Kansan

WINDING LEISURELY OUT OF THE WEST, the Smoky Hill River flowed through Kansas territory which had once been the scene of cattle rustling and Indian fighting. Just north of Junction City it joined the Republican River to form the Kaw.

At Fort Riley, just two miles away, the famed cavalry-man Jeb Stuart was once stationed long enough to bewail the fact that Junction City had no Episcopal Church. Resolved to do something about the situation, he succeeded in stirring up interest in the project, and then helped organize a congregation. An attractive little limestone church, three blocks from the main street, was the result. The Church of the Covenant was the only Episcopal parish of that name in the country.

Robert's Uncle Henry, Judge Pratt, who was Hannah's brother, often contended that Junction City was over-churched. "Why, just look at us!" he told his wife. "We've got a Presbyterian Church, a Methodist Church, a German Reformed Church, a Universalist Church, an Episcopal Church, and —"

But, as his wife pointed out, all the churches seemed well supported. Certainly the Church of the Covenant boasted its small but strong local supporters — town leaders like George Rockwell and blustery old Colonel

McClure. Across the street from the church, for example, stood the great double-winged mansion of the Lees, staunch members of the congregation. Not far away lived an English family, the John Hope Moffatts, themselves loyal members of the Church of the Covenant.

Judge Pratt did not himself belong to the Church of the Covenant, but he was a good friend of men like the Colonel who did. Judge Pratt had written to Robert, inviting his nephew to visit him and his wife. Robert had not seen the Judge since his mother's death, but he well remembered the deep-voiced lawyer-uncle who made toys in his spare time and sent them on to Tunnel at Christmas.

Aunt Josie was sixtyish — slender, silver-haired, and handsome. She came from a strong clan, the Grants. Her brother was a well-known United States marshal in the Yukon. "Your Aunt Josie is a gentle and sweet person," the Judge told young Harry Grant, another nephew who was visiting them that summer, "but I warn you — there's enough Grant in her to make her pretty darned determined on occasion!"

Young Harry Grant was delighted at the prospect of Robert's arrival, and when Robert arrived, the two boys hit it off famously from the start. Life at the Pratt home was a far cry from life at Nashotah or Cowley House or the dormitory at Dickinson. Robert felt completely at home and part of a family again, free to tease and be teased.

One day, soon after Robert had come, Judge Pratt took him around to meet George Rockwell, a vestryman of the Church of the Covenant.

"Your uncle has told you, I assume," said George Rockwell, showing them to the front parlor, "that we have no rector. The church is vacant. We don't even have a lay reader. I think Bishop Millspaugh would be delighted to have you help us out while you are here. I'll write him at once."

And before the week was out, the Bishop's warm response came: "By all means put him on!"

During the summer months which followed Robert not only conducted services at the Covenant but out at Fort Riley as well. The young lay reader became very popular. Many of the young people, it was said, seemed to be taking a greater interest in the church, like Cliff Lee who lived across the street. Young Cliff, who was a member of the choir, liked nothing better than to draw caricatures of people during the service. Robert accidentally picked up Cliff's hymnal one afternoon and found a sketch of himself. It was an unmistakable likeness, and the caption read, R.N.S. PREACHING TO BEAT HELL! Robert laughed, shook his head at the boy's cleverness, and put the hymnal back in the rack, without saying anything about it. But not long after that, Robert did have occasion to reprimand the boy severely. It all happened just after the new electric lights were installed in the church. At evening prayer one Sunday, Cliff slipped out of the choir stalls during the first part of the service and tiptoed around toward the light switches. No sooner had Robert finished one of the first prayers than the church was plunged into Egyptian darkness.

Undaunted, Robert continued the service from memory, beginning appropriately with the words "Lighten our darkness, we beseech thee, O Lord. . . ." When he finished the prayer, the lights came on again. Robert glanced quickly over at the choir stalls. Cliff was missing. As the service continued, he reappeared. Robert knew what had happened. After the service he called the boy to the sacristy.

"Clifford," he said, "you realize of course that what you did was a very serious offense. I'll just make it a police case. My uncle is the police judge here, as you know. I'm sure he will be reasonable."

Cliff looked frightened. "But, sir, I'm — why, I'm a Lee!" he stammered. "What will my mother think if I am called up before the police?"

They talked for some time. Robert was patient and gentle with the boy. Finally, Cliff apologized, and nothing more was said. From that evening on the two became fast friends, and Cliff was won to a new seriousness about the church.

Between frequent trips to Fort Riley, parish calls and services, and occasional dates of an evening, Robert soon managed to gather and prepare the largest confirmation class in the history of the parish — twenty-one people! The townspeople were impressed and delighted.

Late in September, Bishop Millspaugh himself came over for the confirmation service. The church was packed. Judge Pratt and his wife, the Moffatts, the Lees were all there. Both Mr. Rockwell and Colonel McClure were on hand early to make sure everything was in order.

Just before it was time to begin, a young brown-eyed girl slipped into the sacristy.

"Amy Moffatt, what are you doing here?" asked Robert.

"Your surplice is crooked." She gave it a tug. "There," she said with a smile and disappeared. Robert was touched to know of such personal interest in him.

He looked proud as he stood up before the Bishop in the service and said in a clear, strong voice: "Reverend

Father in God, I present unto you these persons to receive the Laying on of Hands."

After the service, Bishop Millspaugh came back to the sacristy to remove his vestments. Mr. Rockwell and the Colonel were standing just inside the door.

"That was the largest confirmation class in the history of the parish. Did you know that?" said Mr. Rockwell, a stickler for statistics.

"Is that so?" said the Bishop. "It was a fine-looking class. Young Spencer seems to be doing good work here."

He finished removing his vestments, put on his coat, and sat down in the large walnut chair by the window.

"I'm glad to be able to see you two alone for a moment," said the Bishop. "I know your young lay reader has been doing a splendid job here. In fact he's done so well that I'm afraid I shall have to replace him."

"Replace him!" roared the Colonel. "Why, you said yourself you thought —"

"My dear Colonel," said the old man, "young Spencer has done so well at building up this church that I think the time has come for you to have a priest."

"But Bishop, you can't take him away!" the Colonel exclaimed.

"Indeed I can," said the Bishop softly.

Colonel McClure tapped his cane on the floor in exasperation. "You are *not* going to take this young man away. We like him — our people want him. He's doing a superb job. You said so yourself. Look at the way he is attracting all those young people, all that new blood, into the church," said Colonel McClure.

"But what about the sacraments?" the Bishop asked him.

"Let a nearby priest come here once a month for Communion," Mr. Rockwell suggested.

The Colonel's face was red. His words were reckless with anger. "Bishop," he said, "if you take young Spencer away, we will close this church!"

"There's no need to shout," said the Bishop softly. He sat silently in the heavy old chair and stared out of the window.

At length, he spoke up. "I'll tell you what I can do," said Bishop Millspaugh. "You understand, I have nothing against the boy."

"We know that," said Mr. Rockwell.

"You couldn't," said the Colonel. "On the contrary, I should think!"

"He may come to study at my Kansas Divinity School in Topeka and finish his studies for the priesthood there."

"How long would he have to be away?" Mr. Rockwell asked.

"Oh, just a few weeks at a time," Bishop Millspaugh explained. "He will be given reading to do. Then he'll return to the church for a few weeks, do the reading in off-duty time, and go back to Topeka again for another study session."

"He would work, earn a salary, and attend school on a kind of back-and-forth arrangement?" asked the Colonel.

"Exactly," said the Bishop.

"That sounds like a splendid plan," said another voice. The men turned. Robert was standing in the door. He had heard the tail end of the conversation, and his own enthusiasm for the idea persuaded the others to accept it.

Robert spent two busy years shuttling the forty miles between Junction City and Topeka.

When he was home in Junction City, he not only had his work at the Covenant and nearby Fort Riley where he was now acting chaplain; he also took services each Wednesday evening at St. John's in Abilene.

Yet that first year Robert was not too busy at Junction City to see quite a lot of young Anne Dillworth — a lovely, blond young woman who belonged to his young people's group at the church. Harry Grant noticed his interest in the girl, and he and his Aunt Josie discussed it with approval.

But Anne soon left for faraway Wells College in Central New York. At first, she wrote to Robert faithfully. There were letters every few days. Then they became less frequent, and when she did write, she spoke more and more of a "brilliant young writer" she had met. At length word reached Junction City that the Dillworth girl was engaged to a young novelist, and Robert never saw her again.

That winter, Robert attended his first church convention at Wichita. Rains came, and there was a dreadful flood. Reports reached Wichita that the Smoky Hill River was at least a mile wide at Junction City, and that the Union Pacific tracks were completely covered. Robert went to Topeka and was marooned there for ten days. All communications were cut off.

Robert later wrote Aunt Josie, "If I ever see Noah — and *he* will certainly make it, if *I* do — I am going to ask him, 'Speaking of floods, were you in the Kaw Valley in 1903?' "

Whenever Robert was in Junction City, he found himself stopping by again and again at the Moffatts' to see young Amy Frances. Amy welcomed those visits. She had a good many young men calling on her — John, the banker's son; Harry, who planned to enter medical school in the fall — but Amy told her mother, "I can talk to Robert about books, poetry, travel, history — not just Junction City gossip all the time!"

As the days grew longer, Robert borrowed a flat-bottomed boat from Sam Hale and took Amy boating on the Smoky Hill River.

As they rowed, Amy talked of her childhood, and told him of her having been at Birkenhead, across the Mersey from Liverpool, England, and about the Moffatts' ownership of a family leather business which was well known throughout England.

Robert was interested to know why the family had left and come to America.

"They came on account of my health," said Amy. "I think Mother has told you that I had a bad case of scarlet fever when I was seven. Well, it caused an aneurysm — it's some sort of dilation of a blood vessel around the heart. It means I have to watch myself pretty carefully."

"But how did you ever end up in Junction City?" Robert asked.

"The doctors told my family that I needed a drier climate. That was all Father needed. He had been itching to come to the United States anyway. So over we came, bringing everything that we owned with us. When we got to Boston, Father saw some intriguing advertisements about 'Kansas — Land of Opportunity.' He inquired around, and the next thing I knew he had bought a ranch at Skiddy — that's right near here."

"I know it. As a matter of fact, I was there only last week," said Robert.

"We didn't stay at Skiddy long, though," Amy said. "The grasshopper plague came, and it was more than we could cope with. The crops were utterly destroyed. Father said we'd just have to move. That's how we happened to come to Junction City." They looked at each other gravely, thinking of the curious pathways by which they had come to this friendship.

Robert and Amy met often that spring, but they had to be careful. In any church, particularly one in a small town like Junction City, any steady association of the preacher's receives a lot of attention. Amy was active in the altar guild at the Covenant, and came in for a lot of teasing speculation and comment on the "special care" she took of the "preacher's" vestments. She was charged with being "sweet on him," but she did not give her feelings away to her companions.

In the Episcopal Church clergy are first ordained deacons, and later priests. On April 5, 1904, the Church of the Covenant was filled to overflowing on the day of Robert's ordination to the diaconate. Bishop Millspaugh was there, together with a number of other Episcopal clergy from nearby towns.

In the solemn service, the old Bishop asked the traditional questions in a firm voice.

Said he, "Do you trust that you are inwardly moved by the Holy Ghost to take upon you this Office and Ministration, to serve God for the promoting of his glory, and the edifying of his people?"

"I trust so," said Robert in a firm voice.

Mrs. Moffatt glanced at her daughter. Amy's eyes were moist.

In less than an hour the ceremony was over. Robert had become a full-fledged deacon. He could now baptize and assist at the Holy Communion but he himself could not yet celebrate the Holy Communion or marry people. Only the priest could do that, and Robert's ordination to the priesthood was still a year off. But he was now the Reverend Robert Nelson Spencer.

"It certainly sounds impressive," Amy told him after the big luncheon given in his honor. "And I like that clerical collar — it suits you."

A few days later, the Reverend Mr. Spencer took off for Binghamton to see his father and other members of his family.

"I rather think Amy hates to see him go," Mrs. Moffatt told her husband the morning Amy went to see Robert off.

"I guess we've all got used to having him around," said Mr. Moffatt.

At teatime, Amy often found herself at the window, watching the street for the familiar spare figure with the slight spring to his step. Mrs. Moffatt, too, missed the young man who always brought a poetic note or a chuckler to the family tea hour.

At Binghamton, Robert had the long-awaited reunion with his father and brothers, and the whole family came out to hear him preach on the first Sunday after his return.

"That was fine, son," said Nelson after the service. He was much moved by his son's power in the pulpit.

"You know, Father," said Robert, "you once gave me the best advice I ever had about preaching."

"I did?" said Nelson Spencer, wonderingly.

"Yes, the night coming back from the Kingsleys' cheese factory," said Robert.

"I don't remember," his father said.

"No wonder," Robert said, with a little laugh. "It happened so long ago. I remember that a thunderstorm came up, and as we were going down that hill near the factory the harness strap broke, remember? You had to stop and lift me down from the wagon. You took the lantern down and told me to hold it for you."

"I believe I remember now," said Nelson.

"Well, you were fixing that strap, and you said to me — I'll never forget it — 'Hold the light, Robbie, so you can see, and then I'll be able to see.' That works for everything, Father. It was the best advice anyone ever gave me."

Nelson shook his head with a smile.

After the first joyful burst of reunion conversation was over, it became obvious to Robert's father that his son was becoming a little homesick for Kansas. Robert talked at length about Junction City and all his friends there, and especially about Amy.

"She has a cameolike face," he told his father eagerly, "and chestnut red hair. When she walks, she has a very dignified way about her — I can't quite describe it. I guess it all comes from having been brought up by English governesses."

As the summer wore on, Robert continued to write Amy regularly. Finally, one homesick August evening he wrote:

DEAR AMY FRANCES,

You have doubtless heard that absence makes the heart grow fonder. Do you also know that absence makes the heart grow bolder? Half a continent away from you for six weeks, this heart has grown fonder and very, very bold.

So bold in fact, that I can now write you what might have made me stammer, if I saw you face to face. Amy, will you marry me? You have been in my thoughts day and night these past weeks. I know it is right. Amy, marry me . . .

I shall await word from you eagerly and will write your mother and father for their consent. Be a good advocate for me, if you can.

My bold heart says "All's well," as I await word from you.

"Do you take this man to be . . . ?" The answer in the Prayer Book is "I do." And I know you to be a loyal churchwoman, Amy. I am certain you will give the right answer!

Bishop Millspaugh will ordain me Priest next June, and we will have the Rectory to live in, and I suppose I shall have a slight increase in salary.

Write me as soon as you decide. Amy, I will be waiting with a quaking and a bold heart. With a devoted spirit, I am Isaac to your Rebekah.

Lovingly,
ROBERT

CHAPTER XIII

That Longest of Sundays

SIX DAYS LATER, Amy's letter arrived with its joyous "I do," and they began making plans at once for a September wedding.

"I don't see how we could be married here," Amy wrote. "We couldn't invite everyone, and if we didn't, there would be hurt feelings. What would you say to St. Peter's Church in Kansas City, Kansas? The Ellises live there, you know, and they are practically members of our family, because they were neighbors of ours in England."

Robert wrote back that he knew the Ellises were wonderful people; St. Peter's was a charming church; and, what's more, the rector was a good friend. The arrangement was agreed upon, and the date set.

Robert later wrote:

I lighted off my train from Upstate New York and Amy lighted off her train in Kansas City, and we were married in St. Peter's Church, Kansas City, Kansas, by the rector, who was an old classmate of mine. The Ellises may be less than kin to Amy, but they were more than kind to both of us. We took the late Union Pacific train to Junction City and were "at home" the next day to all Junction City and Fort Riley . . .

From the start the couple had a life that was far from private. They lived in the same house as the Moffatts, and Robert was, of course, a local clergyman and a public figure. But the people of Junction City were most gracious to the young couple.

Months passed. Then the news got around that Amy was expecting a baby in late June. On June sixth the Bishop came to Junction City to ordain Robert to the priesthood. Amy was not feeling well at the time, but she could not bear to miss Robert's big service.

At last the great moment came for which Robert had prepared so long. He knelt before the altar, and Bishop Millspaugh placed his hands on Robert's head with the words: "Receive the Holy Ghost for the Office and Work of a Priest in the Church of God, now committed unto thee by the Imposition of our hands."

It had been a long journey from Tunnel to this high moment in a little Kansas Church, Amy wrote in her diary, but the moment had come at last, "just as Robert all along felt that it would."

"You know, Amy," Robert said to his wife, "at that altar again today, I sensed that I had never been alone for a moment in that long preparation — even in my lowest moments of depression at Dickinson or Nashotah."

The following week-end, Dr. Fred O'Donnell, the Spencers' doctor, assured Amy that her baby would not come before Monday — and took off for Kansas City.

Sunday — June tenth — was Trinity Sunday. Robert was at the altar, celebrating the Holy Communion, when a friend of the family's came running over from the rectory to the church and up the aisle to Robert.

"You'd better get back to the rectory," she stammered breathlessly. "Amy's — having the baby!"

Robert rushed back to the rectory without stopping to

take off his cassock. But by the time their friend had called him, the delivery was nearly over. Robert found Dr. O'Donnell's associate there.

It was clear Amy was having a hard time of it. Amy's difficult delivery obviously had the doctor gravely upset. "Call Dr. Yates," he said sternly.

Dr. Yates arrived in a matter of minutes. He too looked grave the moment he saw what was happening. The two doctors looked at each other. Amy's heart condition was a cause of special concern.

"Robert, call Dr. O'Donnell at once," said the old doctor. "You can reach him by calling his club in Kansas City. Tell him to bring a surgeon. Frankly, Robert, I'm worried."

Robert was luckily able to reach Dr. O'Donnell at once, and blurted out the story, "She's badly ripped, and hemorrhaging. You must bring a surgeon, and come as soon as you can."

It was dark by the time Dr. O'Donnell and Dr. Perkins, the surgeon, arrived by train in Junction City. A nurse was taking care of the baby. Amy's room was dark. All day long, Robert and the others had kept their despairing vigil. At the arrival of the two doctors from Kansas City, Robert's hope for his suffering Amy revived.

Dr. O'Donnell listened to Amy's labored breathing. He and Dr. Perkins examined her together; she was badly lacerated and was still hemorrhaging.

"We must operate at once, Robert," said Dr. O'Donnell.

Dr. Perkins looked carefully around the house for a suitable operating room. He was slow and meticulous in his attention to what had to be done to prepare for the operation.

Finally, it was decided. "We can rig up an operating table in the kitchen," he told Robert as they came out into the hall. "We'll use the wide ironing board you have in there. It seems to be the best thing to use — it seems to be about the right height from the floor. I'll need Dr. O'Donnell's help and the nurse's. Also, I'll need you. I think you'll have to hold your wife during the operation. Because of her heart, it won't be possible to use an anesthetic."

It took nearly an hour to get everything ready. Amy was carried into the kitchen and placed on the ironing board. It was a hot evening. A moth was flying around the lamplight, and the surgeon slapped at it with his rubber gloves. No one spoke. The nurse held the lamp high, and Robert stood at the end of the ironing board, holding Amy in his arms and whispering encouragement to her.

To Robert, clasping Amy tightly, the operation seemed endless. He knew how great his wife's pain must be and suffered for her. It made him think of Dr. Ward's office and the knife and his father standing there, promising him the overcoat if he did not scream. It was horrible to live through all that again and so much more.

At last the operation was over. Amy, exhausted from her ordeal and the great loss of blood, fell asleep quickly. But she was going to get well. That much they knew, and that was all that mattered. Robert now took time to look at their sleeping baby and turn his eyes to the future. If Amy recovered, he knew that they would feel the baby to have been worth this long and painful Sunday.

CHAPTER XIV

Bout with the "Unpardonable"

SOME TIME LATER, in a letter to the Ellises in Kansas City, Amy wrote:

What a wrench it is to have to pull up stakes and move from Junction City! I suppose you have already heard the news: Robert has accepted the call to St. John's in Springfield, Missouri. I am sad about moving, but Robert knows this is what he should do, and I suppose it really is a step forward for him, and the church looks charming . . .

"And how does it seem to be living in the 'Queen City of the Ozarks'?" Robert asked playfully of his wife as he returned to the rectory on one of their first days in Springfield.

"This is no time to be funny," said Amy. "The drains just broke, and the basement's full of water!"

But despite the basement-flooded rectory, Springfield had many compensations. Robert found his new neighbors "most kind and many of them congenial," he wrote.

Xenophon Hawkins, for example, the tall, gaunt old coal dealer who had once fought with Morgan's Raiders in the Civil War, told Robert on his first Sunday that any time he needed coal for someone who was really down and out, he could just let him know. His coal bins, he said, would be open to him always, on the shortest notice.

Robert did call on him when Joe Colwell lost his job.

Mr. Hawkins was as good as his word — the coal was delivered in half an hour.

Across the street lived Dean E. M. Shepard of nearby
Drury College. Robert spent many a relaxed evening with
President George and the Dean, chatting about everything
from the Civil War to religion and local events.

St. John's drew people not only from within Springfield
but from the country outside as well. One afternoon the
Ozark farmer Cyrus Snead knocked on the door of the
Rectory; his four-year-old son David was with him.

"Just thought I'd git the boy baptized while I was in
town," he said.

During the baptism, young David climbed Robert's
stole like a sailor. And when Robert read the familiar
words about being a faithful soldier and servant, Cy Snead
bellowed, "Well, he'd better be, or I'll larrup him!"

Soon the monotony of rectory routine was broken
again — by a wild-eyed cowboy from a touring rodeo who
appeared at the door late one night. Amy had gone to
bed, but Robert was still working in the study.

Robert invited the cowboy in and the man began at
once to rant and rave at the top of his lungs. Amy heard
the noise and ran to the head of the stairs. She stood
there in terror, listening to the madman threaten to shoot
all the stars out of the flag. She did not know what to do
to help Robert. But as she stood there, paralyzed with
fear, she realized that her husband had, with a joke,
quieted the disturbed man.

"Why not go down to Texas, the Lone Star State?"
Robert had asked. "You'll save ammunition!" The cowboy
laughed, his wildness checked. After a while, Robert was

able to quiet him even further, until he was relatively rational.

"Robert," Amy said when the stranger had gone, "I always knew I had married a poet-preacher. Now, more and more, I see you are really a pastor as well."

About five o'clock one afternoon, Robert happened to be home alone when a handsome foreign car drove up in front of the house. A chauffeur came up to the door.

"Are you Dr. Spencer?" he asked politely.

"Yes, my name is Spencer. I'm a clergyman, not a medical doctor," Robert explained.

"My employer would like to see you," said the man.

A tall, well-dressed gentleman then entered. He introduced himself as J. Wentworth Ramsey from St. Louis, and explained that he and his wife were in Springfield, visiting their daughter for a few days.

Robert showed his guest into his study.

"You are kind to see me," said Mr. Ramsey. "I hope I have not come at a bad time."

"Of course not," Robert assured him. "I was going over some sermon notes. I am glad to have an excuse to forget them for a few moments."

"Frankly, Mr. Spencer, I'm here about my wife," said Mr. Ramsey. "I have heard from my daughter and others about how much you have done to help people. My wife is quite a problem, you see. She is in bad shape mentally, and she's been this way for months."

"Have you been to anyone else about her, Mr. Ramsey?"

"Oh, yes, we've had her before the greatest alienists in this country, mental experts and the like, and they say she has what is called religious melancholia. Have you ever heard of such an ailment?"

"Heavens, yes," said Robert. "I have come across a number of people suffering from it in my ministry. Actually, it's not at all uncommon."

"Maybe so," said Mr. Ramsey, "but my wife has it very badly. Why, my daughter and I took her to Dr. Harcourt Covington, the Fifth Avenue minister, who's become so famous for himself helping people."

"What did he think?"

"He simply dismissed her — he said he was sorry, but he didn't think there was anything wrong with her. 'She's just silly,' he told me!"

Robert was silent for a moment. "Of course, you understand I'm not a doctor or psychiatrist," he said at length, "but if you will bring her to see me, I should be happy to see her."

"She's out in the car now."

"Then do bring her in now."

Mr. Ramsey returned in a moment, leading a gaunt, handsomely dressed woman.

"I'm not going to talk now, Mrs. Ramsey," Robert said smiling, as he showed her to a chair. He nodded to Mr. Ramsey, who took the hint and went out to the car to wait. "I'm not going to talk now — I'm going to listen, Mrs. Ramsey. I want very much to have you tell me your story."

"Well, I've committed the unpardonable sin," she said sobbing, "and I have to go to hell."

Robert smiled. "Well, you can't go tonight," he said. "The last train has gone, and we've got a lot of time to talk this matter over. Just what do you think this unpardonable sin is?"

"A sin for which there is no forgiveness." She put her

handkerchief to her eyes. "I was brought up as a very religious woman in a very religious home. But in recent years, I'm afraid, I've got away from it all. My husband has considerable means. He works hard. In fact, he's away a great deal of the time traveling all over the country on business. In my loneliness I've been throwing my life away in a wild social whirl in New York. It's been a kind of escape from my loneliness."

"Do go on," Robert said quietly.

"One evening in New York, I happened to pass a church where a famous evangelist was speaking — his topic was the Unpardonable Sin. I went in and listened to him. The Unpardonable Sin, he explained, is the one for which you cannot be forgiven, for which Jesus said there could be no forgiveness."

Robert looked at Mrs. Ramsey. He was studying her face. "Yes," he said, "Jesus said you can sin against God, but a sin against the Holy Spirit, for that there is no forgiveness. But you know what that means, don't you? It means final impenitence. It means you haven't even the slightest desire to square accounts for what you've done. You don't want forgiveness."

"It's no use!" Mrs. Ramsey said, sobbing.

"But that's not true, Mrs. Ramsey," Robert continued. "You've been crying here. You've been crying bitterly, and don't you realize that God can see the tear on a human face farther than he can see the biggest star?"

"It's no use!" she cried, shaking her head like a petulant schoolgirl.

"God will forgive you," said Robert. "You don't have to worry about that."

"I don't believe it!" Mrs. Ramsey shrieked. "I don't

believe it! I've committed the Unpardonable Sin. I know it — God knows it! There's no hope!"

"Well, just for the time being, will you do something for me?" Robert asked.

Mrs. Ramsey turned to him, "What's that?"

"Just have a little faith that we can work this thing out," he said.

Mrs. Ramsey stayed on at her daughter's. For months, she met with Robert regularly. Over and over again she repeated her conviction that she was headed straight for hell. Over and over again Robert patiently reminded her that the Christian gospel was the gospel of the second chance for those who were truly sorry.

Mrs. Ramsey seemed sane about most things, but went completely beyond reach when it came to her fixation. She appeared grateful, however, for all the time Robert gave her. One afternoon, she even took off a diamond bracelet and handed it to him. "This is for Mrs. Spencer," she said.

"I can't take that bracelet," Robert protested. "I can't take anything from you, anything at all. Don't you see? I'm doing all of this for your sake. I'm doing all this because our Lord loves you. I can't take anything for it."

Mrs. Ramsey's response was violent; she began to scream and tear her hair in frustration.

Robert said, "All right, then," and put the bracelet in his pocket, after which she calmed down.

When she left, Robert immediately called her daughter. "Your mother gave me a diamond bracelet today. Of course, I can't accept it — I only took it to quiet her, and I'll send it back to you."

Robert's sessions with Mrs. Ramsey continued. No

apparent help seemed to come from the conversations, but, "I still believe your wife will be cured by patience and love," Robert wrote to Mr. Ramsey.

"My wife seems to have a great affection for you," Mr. Ramsey wrote him. "You are the one person in the world she seems to feel is dealing honestly and gently with her."

But whenever Mrs. Ramsey appeared to be showing signs of improvement, something inevitably seemed to happen to undo whatever good had been done. On one occasion she had returned to St. Louis and gave a theater party for a dozen of her husband's business friends and their wives. After an elaborate dinner, the party proceeded to the theater. All seemed to be going well, but when the curtain went up, Mrs. Ramsey rose and screamed her usual self-accusation and fainted. The audience was thrown into an uproar. The performance was halted until Mrs. Ramsey was carried out.

"But what upset you, my dear?" Mr. Ramsey asked his wife later, after she had somewhat recovered.

"I saw all those happy people," she sobbed, "and I realized that I alone — of all the people in the theater — have to go to hell!"

Mr. Ramsey sent for Robert at once. "Please come," he said. "I still feel you are our one hope."

Two days later, Robert arrived on the noon train.

Mr. Ramsey came alone to the station to meet him. "Oh, Mr. Spencer, what can I say?" said Mr. Ramsey. "I had so hoped —"

"Yes, I know," said Robert. "I had, too."

"If there were just something we could do," said Mr. Ramsey. "I've thought of bringing Mary on to visit for a while. Our daughter Mary is an only child, as you know.

She and our little grandson, Johnny, are becoming perhaps the one sane element left in Mrs. Ramsey's life."

"I'm sure of it," said Robert, and fell into thought.

They drove on in silence. As they pulled in the driveway, Robert said, "Don't be surprised at what I do. I've prayed for a long time about this situation. I plan to try a new approach."

"I'll just stay here in the car. You go in alone," said Mr. Ramsey. "I think that would be best."

Robert met Mrs. Ramsey in the front hall. At first she seemed delighted to see him, then somewhat disturbed by his attitude. Robert declined to sit down. He just stood there in the hall, with his worn old black hat in his hand.

"Mrs. Ramsey," he said. "I'm very sorry, but I cannot see you any more. You are going to be one of my first failures. I've tried for three months to convince you that you haven't committed the Unpardonable Sin. You couldn't possibly have committed it. Look at you now. You're crying your eyes out. You are the most penitent person I ever saw."

"It's no use," she said, sobbing.

"I'll wager you have shed more tears than Mary Magdalene," he continued. "But I can't help you any more. I've tried everything. I've pleaded with you again and again. Heaven knows I have prayed for you. I'm afraid I've about got to the end of my resources."

Robert started to leave, then turned as he reached the door. "There is just one further thing that I *could* do that might possibly heal you."

Mrs. Ramsey looked up. "And what's that?" she asked.

"Get you to promise that you will lock your door forever against your daughter Mary," he said.

"But why?" she asked, shocked.

"Why?" Robert continued. "Because she's telling everyone in Springfield that you're ruining her social position. You told me that yourself. She's telling people that you make scenes in the theater, and sometimes scenes on the street. She claims that your going around telling people you know you are damned for ever and ever is a bad influence — enough to keep you from getting well."

He turned to leave, then added, "Unless you lock your door against Mary, I will never see you again."

Mrs. Ramsey looked at him with her wild hawk eyes. Again the tears streamed down her face.

"I could never lock my door against Mary," she sobbed. "She's my child — how could I do such a thing? No matter what she says or does, I couldn't lock my door against her."

Robert grabbed her by both hands and drew her close. "And yet you say that your Heavenly Father has locked His door against you! Don't you see that if you couldn't lock your door against *your* child, God, who is infinitely kinder and more loving than you, or any one of us, could not lock His door against you, His child? Mrs. Ramsey, can't you see *that?*"

She stared into Robert's eyes.

"Say this after me," he continued slowly. "*If I cannot lock my door against my child, God would not lock His door against His child!*"

Mrs. Ramsey repeated the words after him slowly, never once taking her eyes from his.

Later that afternoon, Robert told Mr. Ramsey: "She repeated those words, and you could almost see the peace begin to come back into her eyes. But she is not cured.

Don't misunderstand me," Robert went on. "It will take a long time. But I do believe the recovery has begun. It was as though she'd had a blow on the head and a splinter lodged in her brain. My job was to probe patiently till we found the splinter and a way to remove it. Now I believe we may have found that way."

"Do you know what you will have done?" Mr. Ramsey asked as they drew up to the station. "Your trip here will have helped bring a whole family out into the sunlight of normal living."

Robert smiled. "Your wife's struggle is not over yet, but I think she's on her way. No, Mr. Ramsey, I didn't do a thing. I couldn't have. It was God who did that work — God and your wife, working together."

"But you were the one who —"

"I'll give your love to Mary," said Robert smiling. "I must be off. There's the last call for the train."

In a moment he had disappeared into the dust and shadows of the dark station.

CHAPTER XV

"Tell It unto No Man"

NOT ONLY IN SPRINGFIELD but elsewhere in the diocese Robert was developing quite a reputation as a speaker.

"He speaks so easily," said Mrs. Walter Jones one afternoon at the Guild tea.

"Easily!" Amy exclaimed. "You have no idea how hard he works over his sermons. He spends hour after hour writing them out."

"But when he stands up to preach —"

"When he stands up to preach," Amy continued, "of course, he's likely to change the whole talk around."

Robert was a voracious reader and had a habit of taking books down from the shelf, reading a chapter or two in several of them, then hurrying off to some appointment without replacing them.

"No wonder the living room looks as though a cyclone had hit the place," Amy said in apology to her mother. "Robert's left a book on every stick of furniture in the room, but I'm used to it."

And Amy said she was used to Robert's occasional intrusions in the kitchen at odd hours between appointments. "Robert wanders out to the kitchen with a scrap of paper," said Amy. "He's done it a thousand times. He'll just stand there leaning against the door. He'll run his fingers through that wild mop of hair of his and say, 'Amy, how does this sound?' "

Saturday afternoons, week in and week out, Robert regularly read his sermon for the next morning to Amy. When he finished, if the weather was clear, he made a practice of taking the baby for long walks. At first, these meant pushing a carriage. Later, as Kathleen learned to walk by herself, these meant "excursions" — little adventures that Robert looked forward to all week.

"He's cruel, Amy!" Mrs. Moffatt exclaimed, as she watched Robert and Kathleen from the window.

"What are you talking about?" Amy asked, coming from the kitchen.

"He's torturing that poor little girl, Amy. Robert's hiding behind that big maple tree over there. See, Kathleen's looking for him. Poor dear, she's scared!"

"Nonsense, Mother, Kathleen knows her father's just playing hide-and-seek with her."

Robert darted out from behind the tree, and Kathleen ran out to him and hugged him.

"Just the same," said Mrs. Moffatt, "I think he's cruel."

"I don't," said Amy, "and I don't think Kathleen does either."

Amy told Robert about the conversation. "A good thing Mother wasn't here the time you preached the sermon about how babies can hang from trees!" she said, recalling one of Robert's first sermons in Springfield, in which he had said that even a small baby can hang from a tree.

Old Mr. Hawkins had waited for him at the door after the service.

"I can't go along with you on that business about babies hanging from trees," he said sharply.

"You can't?" Robert asked. He ran next door, picked Kathleen out of her crib and hurried back to Mr. Hawkins.

"Watch this," he said as he wrapped his baby's hands around the branch of a tree. Kathleen did hang on. She could support her own weight.

Mr. Hawkins gawked. "All right," he said grumpily. "You win. Maybe next time you'd better take her into the pulpit with you!"

Robert had been rector of St. John's for two years when he stood up one Sunday morning to say good-by.

"I will always have a warm sense of gratitude for the happiness you have given Mrs. Spencer and me here in the 'Queen City of the Ozarks,'" he said quietly from the chancel steps, and told the story behind his move.

Earlier that week, Bishop Atwell had called him. "The rector of Trinity Church in Kansas City is leaving for Washington," he said. "The church is in bad shape — it's carrying a tremendous load of debt. The population is changing, and the problems his successor has to face will be very great, I'm afraid. This job's going to call for sacrifice. Are you interested?"

"Me!" Robert exclaimed.

"The vestry wants you," said the Bishop, "and I think they're right. I'm convinced you're the man for the job."

Robert and the Bishop talked at some length. "May I call you back?" Robert asked. "I'd like to talk this over with my wife."

Amy did not seem overjoyed at the news about Kansas City, but she knew the decision was Robert's to make, and wanted it so.

"Of course — if you really believe we are supposed to go . . ." she said softly, then slipped upstairs to tuck Kathleen in for the night.

"Amy's a rare woman, Bishop," said Robert when he spoke to the Bishop again. "We'll be in Kansas City as soon as we can."

"I'm never going to like you!" a Mrs. Denninger, one of the parishioners, told the new rector as he stood at the door after the first service. "We really loved dear Dr. Talbot," she said.

"I'm sure you did," said Robert.

After their first month there, Robert told Amy that Bishop Atwell may have tried to paint a realistic picture of what the problems at Trinity would be like, but he had certainly not told them all that he might have about the difficulties of the changing neighborhood and the deplorable financial status of the parish. Robert's salary was very modest, and the Spencers found it hard sledding to meet the monthly payment of fifty dollars for the house. Amy managed as best she could, economizing on food and clothing wherever possible. She made all of Kathleen's clothes. She worked hard around the house but still managed to help Robert by putting in many hours of work at the church as well.

From the moment he arrived in Kansas City he was incredibly busy. The vestry seemed to have been storing up long years of problems waiting for some new rector to come along and assume them. Busy as he was trying to solve the problem of how to raise money for the church, Robert made certain that nothing interfered with his pastoral counseling. He was not only faithful about calling on the sick but also on all the other old-timers in the neighborhood and all the newcomers he could find. He began to carry a phonograph with him on sick calls with the idea that music would soothe the sick. It soothed him as well.

"God when he made me didn't put music in my soul," he told Amy — "just a great hunger for it."

Once, when contractors who were building new streets lacked funds and made strong appeals for volunteers to come help, Robert signed up and went out on a road-building gang for a week. But before long, his arm began to give out under the strain.

"You've got to give this up," his doctor said. "It's doing you harm."

Robert gave up the work, but the example he had set had already won him new admirers in the city.

That Sunday, Robert announced as his appropriate sermon text: *Whither have ye made a road today?*

One morning, a distinguished-looking gentleman came to Robert's study in a state of distraction. He introduced himself as Norton Parker, and burst immediately into a torrent of weeping.

"I've killed my wife! I've killed my wife!" he cried.

Slowly, Robert put the pieces of the story together. Mr. and Mrs. Parker, it seems, used to alternate between going to Europe one summer and spending the next at their ranch. Mrs. Parker had had a very bad heart condition; there had been three coronary thromboses in two years.

This particular year, the Parkers had been due to go abroad, but Norton Parker had insisted they go to the ranch instead. There had been quite a squabble over it, but Norton had won. The Parkers went to the ranch, Mrs. Parker had another heart attack, and died.

"She died," Mr. Parker said sobbing, "because we were thirty-five miles from any doctor. If we'd only gone to Europe, we'd have been able to get hold of a doctor at once, and Margaret would have been alive today."

Robert listened quietly to the man, then said firmly, "Well, in the first place, that's absurd. Even if your wife had had twelve of the best doctors around her bed, she'd have died of that attack. She'd had them before. You've told me enough about the case to convince me that she was far beyond the aid of any doctor. *You* didn't kill her."

"But I did, don't you see? I killed Margaret!"

Robert saw Norton Parker regularly for months. Every time it was the same story: "I killed my wife!" Every time Robert patiently heard him through the whole story again and exhausted some new argument trying to convince the man that he was not responsible for his wife's death.

Finally, one cold January noon when Mr. Parker came in for one of their talks, Robert told him not to remove his coat. "I'll get my own hat and coat. They're in the closet," he said. "We're both going out."

"Where are we going?" Norton Parker asked.

"I want you to come with me," he said. "We're going to see the District Attorney," said Robert.

"But why?"

"Why? Because you have finally convinced me that you did murder your wife. That makes me an accessory after the fact, Mr. Parker. I know now that it's my duty to take you to the District Attorney, much as I dislike having to do it. Come on now."

Norton Parker looked at him, stunned for a moment, then burst out laughing. "But how absurd!" he exclaimed. "How utterly absurd!"

"That is precisely what I've been trying to convince you about for the past three months!" Robert said smiling.

Norton Parker stood there, stunned for a moment. "You have no idea, Mr. Spencer, what you have done," he said.

"I have done nothing," said Robert. "If you feel any cause for thanks, you may prefer to go out into the nave and kneel down and give thanks there — where they're due. In fact, I'd like to join you, if I may." And they slipped out into the darkened church.

Robert had little time for reading. These days it was all he could do to scribble a few notes in his sermon book during the week. As a result, oftentimes he found himself sitting up late Saturday night putting his sermon together for Sunday.

The sparrow hath found an house, and the swallow a nest for herself, where she may lay her young, even thine altars, O Lord of hosts.

Robert wrote those words from the Eighty-fourth Psalm in his sermon notebook one frigid January morning.

January 1912 was one of the most bitterly cold months on record in Kansas City. It halted the digging of the approaches to the new Union Station and threw hundreds of men out of work for three weeks. The migratory workers were housed in flophouses in the north end of town which were heated by natural gas. The heat had failed in the extremely cold weather, and as a result, the diggers had been frozen out of the flophouses onto the street to sleep in police stations or doorways. The majority of them had no overcoats as the thermometer went down to new record lows.

One morning on his way to church on the trolley, Robert spotted one of these workers trying to protect his face from the wind with a ragged sleeve. Robert got off the trolley and went to the nearest phone to call the Chief of Police.

"Can you round up these men?" Robert asked. "We will make a dormitory, and we'll keep them there until the cold spell's over. I'll set up a kitchen and arrange to feed them. We'll be glad to have them stay in the church basement —and we won't even ask them to go upstairs into the church, if they don't want to."

He called Amy. "We need a soup kitchen for the migratory workers as fast as we can get it. The police are rounding them up. They'll be here in a few minutes. See if you can get together enough people to help you."

Robert had to act quickly; there was no telling how soon the men would begin to appear. He called up a large wholesale furniture house and rented two hundred cots. Mrs. Denninger and the others arrived to help Amy keep the soup and coffee piping hot and ready for when the men arrived. High school students came in to help with the project, and set to, putting up the cots.

Then the men began to arrive by the dozens. Amy and her volunteers served the first hot meal.

Robert, sensing the men's uneasy gratitude, spoke up. "Men, welcome to Trinity Church. We are happy to feel we can help you during this appalling cold spell in which so many of you must have suffered."

The men looked at each other self-consciously.

"Those of you who use tobacco," Robert continued, "please feel free to smoke. If you don't have tobacco and want some, I'll see that you get it."

His words seemed to break the ice, and the men appeared more relaxed.

The opening of the church to the suffering men attracted wide publicity. Headlines like A SQUARE INSTEAD OF A SERMON, A PIPE INSTEAD OF A PREACHMENT and OPENS FASHIONABLE CHURCH TO THE HOMELESS appeared above stories of the project. Blustery Colonel William Rockhill Nelson, publisher of the *Kansas City Star*, sent a reporter to interview the young preacher and get the story.

Robert was no help to the man. "This is Christ's house. He would have taken them in," he said. "And if He had been interviewed by the *Kansas City Star*, He'd probably have said what He said many other times: 'See that you tell it unto no man.' You can thank Colonel Nelson for me, but there *is* no story."

When the reporter went back to Colonel Nelson and told him what had happened, the publisher banged the desk with his fist. "By God, you go tell that young preacher he can have everything the *Star* has."

But not everyone was equally impressed with what Robert was doing. One minister told his congregation, "It's all wrong. A church is a place for worship, not for bunks and soup kitchens. Young Spencer is exposing his congregation to vermin and disease. He's making the church into a veritable flophouse. And is this, brethren, is this the true mission of the church?"

"You look tired, dear," Amy said late one evening when at last the cold spell had passed. Both Amy and Robert had worked long hours those three weeks, and they were both exhausted.

Amy sat on the arm of Robert's chair. He was leafing through the sermon notebook.

"Look at this," he said. *"The sparrow hath found an house, and the swallow a nest for herself, where she may lay her young, even thine altars, O Lord of hosts.* Those weren't all sparrows or swallows who flocked to Trinity for sanctuary," he said smiling, "but some of them were certainly birds."

At the eleven o'clock service the following Sunday, Robert used an original prayer. "It just seemed to fit," he said later.

Eternal Father, Who hath so ordered Thy universe that everything in it, from anthill to archangel, is always lifting something; may we so lift our weary hearts to Thee, that they may be lifted into everlasting peace.

Mrs. Denninger met him at the door the moment the service was over. "You have no idea what you have come to mean to us," she said. "You are what we really needed. I hope we shall always be friends."

CHAPTER XVI

Epworth Heights

KATHLEEN WAS GROWING UP. She went to school now and seemed to enjoy it.

A public issue came up involving teachers; the *Star* ran editorials about it, and dinner parties around town echoed and re-echoed the debates pro and con. At school, Kathleen's teacher came up to her and said, "Your father is a very public-spirited man. I hope you'll go home and tell him to be sure to go and vote on this issue."

"Miss Smith," said Kathleen, "I'm awfully sorry. He won't have time, I'm sure. Mother has been after him for weeks now to have his hair cut, and he can't even find time for that!"

For Robert's calendar became fuller as time went on. New committees, more and more addresses, and numerous assignments for Bishop Sidney Catlin Partridge — all this work was piled on top of his duties as rector of Trinity.

"I can't believe we're actually leaving," said Amy when the Spencers finally left the city for their first summer vacation at Epworth Heights, Ludington, Michigan. They had heard the senior warden at Trinity talk so much about the place that they had decided to give it a try.

The trip was quite a jaunt for widowed old Mrs. Moffatt, who looked more like Queen Victoria every day. The

Spencers took the day train to Chicago, then climbed
aboard tobacco-chewing Captain Stufflebeam's old *Illinois,*
which landed them at Ludington on Lake Michigan at six
the next morning. A quick breakfast and a ride over to
Epworth Heights on the little "dummy" shuttle train, and
there they were at Epworth, "This Place of Light," at last.

As Robert years later wrote from France, "The watering
places of Europe do not hold a candle to Epworth. No
wonder we both fell in love with the place from the start.
The simplicity of life, the setting, the people — I long to
be back there."

Epworth Heights had started as a camp-meeting spot,
then became a meeting place for the Epworth League
when that was the great Methodist youth organization.
Later, as the Chautauqua movement mushroomed out
across the country, Epworth became a Chautauqua. Here
great musicians gave concerts in the Auditorium each
summer. Celebrated theatrical groups like Ben Greet's
Shakespearean players from Stratford-on-Avon gave plays
each summer in the natural amphitheater.

The Spencers rented a dilapidated cottage down by the
lake for the lordly sum of seventy-five dollars for the season. What it boasted in the way of a view it lacked in
creature comforts. The roof leaked, the plumbing was
atrocious, the sofa upholstery was coming apart. Jacob's
pillow of stone, Robert said, had nothing on the hardness
of the cottage beds.

Epworth teemed with children of Kathleen's age. She
spent the morning, and a good part of the afternoon after
her nap, on the beach. Robert told Mrs. Moffatt he had
never seen Amy happier than she seemed up at the lake.

"That's understandable, Robert," said the old lady.

"Amy spent her early years on the Mersey, and once you've lived by water, I don't think you are ever quite happy away from it."

As Robert and Amy sat by the lake one day, watching Kathleen playing with her friends, they saw Bishop Quayle come in from the lake and beach his great white boat. He shook the mist from his mane of hair, went to his cottage, then reappeared a few moments later dressed in his black Prince Albert coat and a pair of white duck trousers which were spotlessly clean except for a few iron stains from contact with the rusted oarlocks. Under his arm he carried some books. William A. Quayle was a kind of unofficial patron saint around Epworth. He was known as "The Skylark of Methodism."

"Isn't this lake magnificent?" he asked the Spencers as he paused beside them. "I call it 'the blue vein in the palm of God.'"

Robert agreed, and then asked him, "Where are you off to with those books?"

"Why don't you come along?" said Bishop Quayle. "I'm lecturing on Browning every afternoon this week."

Amy stayed behind to watch Kathleen, but Robert went with the Bishop, and each afternoon that week he showed up promptly at four to attend the lecture. Bishop Quayle gave a different lecture series at Epworth every summer — on a play of Shakespeare, the life of William the Silent or Oliver Cromwell perhaps, Napoleon's retreat from Moscow, a topic like "Forgotten Yesterdays of Literature."

Robert came to admire the Bishop greatly, and confided to Amy that the man had become a kind of idol of his. "How I should like to preach like him!" he said with feeling.

Robert used his vacation for reading and writing, not all
of it by any means serious. One of the lighter verses he
wrote concerned man's banishment from Eden:

> Hearken well, my hearers,
>   Lest ye sin in pride.
> Beasts are still in Eden,
>   Man alone outside.
>
> Angel's flashing swordsplay
>   Guards that early Grail!
> Tremble, apple eaters!
>   Fido, wag your tail.

Robert also enjoyed the swimming and the golf. Despite
his weak right arm, he managed to play a game in the 80's
and was runner-up in the golf tournament.

Amy teased Robert about "going headlong into hell
every Sunday." In those days, at Epworth the congregation regularly recited the Apostle's Creed but carefully left
out the phrase "descended into hell." Robert was not
used to leaving out the phrase.

"As a result, what happens?" said Amy. "There you go,
one of the only Episcopalians present, headlong into hell,
leaving all the Methodists high and dry behind you. I hope
you won't disgrace us again this morning!"

"Who's preaching?" Robert asked.

"An Archibald Something-or-other," said Amy.

All during the service, Robert studied the visiting
preacher's face, and at times felt the Methodist minister
return his regard. At the end of the service, Robert made
his way forward to speak to him.

"You wouldn't be Robert Spencer from Dickinson,
would you?" the minister asked.

"I am," said Robert, "and you are Arch Holmes!"

This was the first time the two men had seen each other since the fateful incident in college when they had both been called up before the President on a charge of disorderly conduct.

Arch rushed forward and put his arms around Robert. "Gosh, but it's been a long time since Molly Pitcher's grave!"

War in Europe came, and with it mounting tension which spread throughout the world. The summer headlines, in 1916, telling of a second Battle of the Somme, German sabotage in New Jersey, and trouble on the Mexican border seemed to cast storm clouds over Ludington. One sensed this restlessness in conversations on the beach and at the supper parties.

At the end of the summer, when his Methodist neighbors invited Robert to preach at the auditorium, he spoke on the text: *If I take the wings of the morning, and dwell in the uttermost parts of the sea; even there shall thy hand lead me, and thy right hand shall hold me.*

Robert that day described the sinking of the *Titanic*.

"On that fateful day the ship was warned as early as nine o'clock in the morning that there was ice to the west, but the wireless operator was casting up his accounts and did not even take the trouble to write down the message. We must not blame him. He believed, like everyone else, that he was on an 'unsinkable ship.' Later a warning came which he did send up to Mr. Ismay, managing director of the White Star Line, who was on the bridge. Mr. Ismay smiled and put the message in his pocket. Other warnings followed and three hours before the *Titanic* struck there was an insistent warning to reduce speed and to change course. To that warning, the *Titanic's* operator replied, *Shut up and keep out! I am talking to Cape Race, and you are jamming my signals!* Then came the disaster: a great mountain of ice, three-fourths submerged, loomed up; and the 'unsinkable ship' ran upon that great sword of ice running out into the sea, and was ripped from prow to stern."

Robert leaned over the edge of the pulpit. "My friends," he said soberly, "we must remember that there is nothing in this universe that is unsinkable, save only God. This nation can endure if its people are vigilant, neighborly, and cooperative. There are today warning voices, and they may be becoming a little tiresome, but let us not neglect them. Let us not say: *Shut up and keep out! I am talking to Vanity Fair, and you are jamming my signals!*"

Early the next morning, the Spencers left for Kansas City.

CHAPTER XVII

"Poverty Hill" and Lambeth

ROBERT SERVED AS RECTOR of Trinity for eight years from 1909 to 1917. He made his influence felt in a number of ways, not only among his parishioners but elsewhere throughout the city. For instance, he personally set up and ran a sanitarium during the meningitis epidemic; he tackled a huge civilian work load during the war years; and he frequently contributed poems and articles to the columns of the *Star*.

During this period the West Side of Kansas City was said to be fast becoming a blighted neighborhood. What had once been known as "Quality Hill" people now referred to as "Poverty Hill," because the wealthy families of earlier years had moved away to the new residential districts to the south. As the neighborhood changed, first one Baptist church, then one Lutheran church closed its doors. Only the Roman Catholic Cathedral and Grace Episcopal Church remained.

One morning in 1917 Bishop Partridge sent for Robert and told him of his plan to merge Trinity with Grace Church.

"Better to make one chimney smoke where two smoked before," said the Bishop. "Trinity is struggling along, and Grace has all but gone on the rocks."

"Do you plan to close Trinity altogether and move

us over to the Grace Church building?" Robert asked.

"Yes," said the Bishop, "and what's more I've talked it all over with the people at Grace. They want you to be rector of the new Grace and Holy Trinity Church."

"Bishop, I don't know that that would be wise," said Robert. "Wouldn't it be better to have me resign, and have a new man from the start?"

"No, Bon Pasteur," said the Bishop smiling. "The Grace people know you and want you. The Trinity people seem devoted to you."

Reluctantly, Robert agreed to lead the combined congregation.

At Trinity the news of the merger created a furor. One of the vestrymen, Mr. Fuller, and a group of the old parishioners entered Robert's study, took the seal of the parish, and wrote to the Church Building Fund Commission that "some of the congregation has left, but we still have a vestry and will take over the paying of interest and principal on the loan."

For two years after the official merger, Mr. Fuller and his cohorts continued to send a special delivery letter which arrived at Robert's house each Saturday, telling him that he would be expected to conduct services at Trinity the next day.

The Bishop said repeatedly to Robert: "Pay no attention. You are to conduct services at Grace."

"The row over the merger has been hard on Robert," Amy wrote a friend. "It wasn't easy after eight years to tear himself away from Trinity, but Robert felt the merger was right. All during this furor, I've kept thinking of the first-century historian Robert told me about who said 'Behold, how these Christians love one another!'"

The first Sunday in October that Robert held services at Grace, the weather was bitter cold. As the furnace was not working very well, the new rector hurried over to the church at daybreak and, with the help of the sexton, managed to repair it in time to get the church warm enough for services.

But the pair discovered that there wasn't enough coal to last an hour.

Robert immediately called the coal dealer, with apologies for disturbing him so early and on a Sunday at that. Within two hours, the emergency coal arrived.

At the eleven o'clock service, Robert spoke to a congregation of seventy-five in the church which could seat a thousand!

"Our only hope of saving this church," he said from the pulpit, "lies with those people who have moved away but who may still feel an attachment for the parish and will help us gather an endowment. Indeed, if I am to stay here, I want a little more than that sum. If we believe we should keep the Cross on this great metropolitan Church, I should like to see us spend enough money to put four gargoyles on the corners of the tower" — and here he suited the gesture to the words — "four gargoyles, thumbing their noses at the four corners of Kansas City and saying 'We are going to stay right here!'"

After lunch that day, Robert's telephone rang. "I heard your sermon," said a woman's voice. "I am one of those people you talked about who still feel an attachment to the church. I am putting a check in the mail for twenty-five thousand dollars toward the endowment fund."

"But who — who are you?" Robert stammered.

"Mrs. William Rockhill Nelson," said the voice. "You

know, my husband and I have never forgotten the way you took those homeless men into the church when you first went to Trinity."

"Who called you?" Amy asked, seeing her husband so affected.

Robert could not speak. He went to the window and stood there, looking out at the afternoon sunlight on the grass, and there Amy joined him, content to wait until he would tell her his astonishing news.

The year 1920, which ushered in the so-called "flapper" age, saw the names Sacco and Vanzetti make headlines on murder charges; it saw the publication of *This Side of Paradise*, a first novel by F. Scott Fitzgerald, and *Main Street*, a satire of life in a small midwestern town by Sinclair Lewis; it saw air mail service established for the first time between the East and West coasts.

In Episcopal circles, 1920 was the year of another Lambeth Conference of Anglican bishops from all over the world. Every ten years these bishops gather in England for discussions of such matters as theology, doctrine, problems of the Church, social improvements, or possible union with Churches of other communions. The conference has no legislative powers and can only make recommendations. T. S. Eliot has said that on such occasions one has the feeling that the Church of England is washing its dirty linen in public; but, he points out, the linen through such a conference does seem to get washed. The Lambeth Conference is in fact world news when it is held, and indeed afterwards, for it does have a strong influence on the whole Anglican Communion — of which the American Episcopal Church is a part.

When Bishop Partridge decided to take Robert as his chaplain to England to the Lambeth Conference in 1920, Robert asked Amy, "Do you think that you'll be all right?"

"Of course, we'll be all right," said Amy. "Kathleen and I will be up at Epworth. We'll miss you, but we'll be fine."

Robert's parishioners said they thought it a great honor for him to be chosen to go with the Bishop, and presented him with a purse to help with his expenses.

Securing his tickets and passport, winding up his affairs at the church for the summer, and doing his last-minute packing would have been enough to fill those last few days in June before he and the Bishop were scheduled to leave. But at the last minute two impacted wisdom teeth acted up, and Robert had to go down to the dentist and have them out.

"You can go," said the doctor with some misgiving, "but you're liable to be rather uncomfortable for a while. I'm going to give you some medication to take with you."

Finally, the day came. Amy and Kathleen took Robert to the station, where the Bishop was waiting somewhat impatiently for him.

"Robert will have to go light on the eating," Amy explained to the Bishop. "He had two teeth out, you know. I'm afraid he won't be able to manage much more than milk toast for a few days."

On the *Ile de France* two days later, the dining salon steward suggested that Robert try French bread sopped in wine.

"*On dit* it is much better than milk toast," he said smiling.

Robert took the waiter's suggestion and confessed to the Bishop it made the meal hour more pleasant.

A chaplain at Lambeth "waits" on his bishop. Although he is not allowed to sit in the conference sessions, he has the privilege of attending all other functions — and there are many — and doing such work as the Bishop may require.

At Lambeth, Robert met scores of bishops — bishops from Australia, New Zealand, India, Japan, Canada, the United States, bishops from all over the world, many of them nattily dressed in Episcopal aprons and gaiters.

Robert wrote to Amy almost daily about his experiences, his meetings with one and another notable, his visits to this or that famous landmark. "I must admit," he said, "that at our formal functions I have to chuckle every time I hear someone announce 'The Lord Bishop of Arkansas!' "

On the eve of the fourth of July, Robert was invited to the annual dinner given by the American merchants of London and found himself seated next to the distinguished poet-playwright, John Drinkwater. In his letter to Amy the next day Robert said that Mr. Drinkwater was most grateful to Americans for the warm reception they had given his play about Lincoln. Drinkwater, Robert said, regarded Lincoln as the most tragic figure in history except for the "Martyr of Golgotha."

And speaking of Lincoln, [Robert continued] I must admit that I get a thrill every time I pass that glorious statue of him at the Abbey. I have been passing that statue for days and have noticed a beautiful wreath of flowers on it. Today I was told that those flowers were placed there by an African missionary. Thus, another continent has been added to the rosary of reverence from which Abraham Lincoln's cross is hung.

Robert had to stick close to London during the weeks of the conference, but one day he received an invitation to preach at Oxford. He was flattered and accepted at once.

That evening, he excused himself from his colleagues and returned to his Notting Hill lodging to work on his sermon. He decided to preach on the theme *Consider the lilies* and began by pointing out how the beauty of the lilies do preach of God's providential care.

He looked at what he had written. "England needs strength today in her sanctuaries as well as beauty," he wrote on a card and propped it up against the inkwell before him.

"But do lilies *do* anything?" he asked himself.

He looked across the room at a few books he had brought with him. He recognized them all except one little green book. Whose was that? Why had he brought that along? He walked over and picked it up. It was a book which had been out of print for some time. Flipping through the pages he came on a story of a stag hunt in France.

The hounds had pursued the poor stag to the river and to an island, where for a few minutes the hunted stag was able to stand off the first dogs. Then, plunging again into the stream, the stag swam to the farther bank, broke through the underbrush and emerged into acres of lily-blooms! In vain in that fragrance the hounds tried to follow the scent of the stag. Finally they went baffled away.

So there was salvation in the lilies! So there was "sanctuary, safety, haleness, a holiness in beauty as well as a beauty in holiness!"

The trip to Oxford, undertaken with grave misgivings, proved rewarding in every way. Not only did the sermon go well, but the trip marked the end of Robert's dental trouble. In a garden at Oxford he pulled out the last root of wisdom tooth, which had been bothering him, and he returned to London in high spirits.

The Lambeth meetings and receptions went on and on. One afternoon Robert and John Dallas, another priest, decided they had had enough.

"Let's duck out and take in the fights," Robert whispered in the hall. "They'll never miss us."

John agreed. They hurried back to the hotel, changed clothes, grabbed a quick supper, then quietly slipped over to the arena and went in through a side door.

"They'll never miss us," Robert said again.

"They won't?" said John. "Look over there!" He pointed across the ring. One whole section was packed with clergy who had decided to duck out and play hooky, too. "Why, I do believe I even see the 'Lord Bishop of Arkansas'!" John said, chuckling.

As the Lambeth Conference wore on, Amy detected from his letters that Robert was homesick. "What I wouldn't give for a little hash or a peanut butter sandwich! We've had nothing but roast beef since we got here."

When at last the time came to sail, Robert sent word to Amy to stay on at Epworth, so that the three of them might have a few days' reunion there together before he returned to work.

"Do you think he likes England, Mother?" Kathleen asked.

"Oh, yes, he likes England all right," said Amy, "but I'm sure he would take a day on the beach at Epworth to an overheated London full of bishops any time."

CHAPTER XVIII

Sinclair Lewis and *Elmer Gantry*

IN SEPTEMBER OF 1922, Robert was attending the General Convention in Portland, Oregon, when the bellboy brought him a telegram.

Robert tore open the envelope. It was Kathleen! Amy wired that their daughter was seriously ill. "Emergency appendix" was the diagnosis.

"I can tell Amy's frantic!" Robert told one of the delegates, and rushed out of the room, down the stairs, and out of the hotel. He did not stop for his hat, coat, luggage, or anything, but ran all the way to the station to try to get a train out that night.

"Sorry, there's nothing tonight," said the ticket agent. "But there's a train out first thing tomorrow."

Robert spent a sleepless night. He packed, told the other clergymen the news, then checked out of the hotel. He was down at the station fully an hour ahead of departure time.

Finally, the train took off. Robert had wired Amy which train he would take, and so, all along the way at different stations, the porter brought him telegrams from her, reporting on Kathleen's "critical condition."

Near him on the train sat a young woman whose sister had just been operated on the day before for appendicitis.

The second day out, the porter came looking for Robert in the dining car.

"Come quick, Padre," he said. "That lady's awful upset. I just gave her a wire I picked up at the last stop. Padre, her sister's dead. Could you talk to her?"

"Dead!" Robert jumped up and weakly followed the porter back to the Pullman where the hysterically sobbing girl had been shown to a drawing room.

For three hundred miles Robert tried to comfort the grief-stricken girl, all the time wondering about his own Kathleen. But the more he spoke to the girl about her loss, the more certain he became that everything would be all right.

When at last he reached Kansas City, the danger for Kathleen was past. Dr. Harold Kuhn met him at the door of the hospital. "She's going to be fine," he said smiling. "She's doing nicely."

One evening in the spring, the parents of a young theological student, home for vacation, asked Robert and Amy to dinner.

After dinner, young Ralph, full of a long winter of seminary classes, asked Robert, "Why do you suppose our Lord took His followers out of Bethany before His Ascension?"

Robert smiled. "Do you have a map of the United States handy?" he asked.

Ralph's father went to the bookshelves and produced an impressive atlas. "Here, will this do?"

"Fine," said Robert, opening the book to a large map of North America. He took a pencil from his pocket. "Let me run my pencil across this map until it rests on Mount

Vernon, there by the Potomac. What does that mean? It means the word — Washington."

Ralph looked at him, puzzled.

"Now I'm putting the pencil on Lexington, Massachusetts," he continued. "What does that mean?"

"The shot heard round the world?"

"Yes, or the Minute Men," said Robert. "And take Springfield, Illinois. What does that mean?"

"Lincoln."

"Exactly. We can never escape the implications, the memories of localities."

"I see, but what does this have to do with Bethany?" Ralph asked.

"No one who had been with Jesus for any length of time could have been led out of Bethany without being thrilled with its memories. There had been a home there, the home of Mary and Martha and Lazarus."

Robert said the theology of the Ascension is apt to trouble a person. Where is our ascended Lord? Where is heaven? Is it up or down or in or out?

"In our geography as Christians," he continued, "I like to think it is 'as far as Bethany.' After all, Bethany was our Lord's second home. It was where His friends Mary and Martha and Lazarus lived. It was where He spent some time with His disciples. As I see it, that's why He led them out as far as Bethany. They would always remember that He was at home with them."

"And home is heaven enough, I suppose, when we are safely folded in it," said Ralph's mother.

"With Him," Robert added.

Finally, the Spencers rose to leave.

"I envy your faith, Mr. Spencer," said Ralph's father as

he showed them to the door. "I wish I could believe more deeply in a God I cannot see."

"Someone once asked an Arab how he could believe in such a God," said Robert, "and he replied by saying 'Why do I believe that a traveler passed my tent last night? I can see his footprints in the sand!' "

The publicity Robert had been given, years before, about the way he sheltered homeless men in his church, the sanitarium he set up during the meningitis epidemic, his frequent preaching on "skid road," Friday afternoon services he held specially for the sick, his work now as chaplain of St. Luke's hospital — all made him well known as a devoted pastor who cared about "those who are any ways afflicted, or distressed, in mind, body, or estate," as the prayer book puts it. A good many people around town knew, for example, how many times Robert had picked up one former rich man, an alcoholic, from the gutter and personally paid for his "drunk cures." As one man said, "It's just useless to give Robert a shirt. He'll give it to the first tramp who hasn't one."

Amy and Kathleen were downtown shopping one afternoon when Robert showed two unexpected callers to his study. Pushing open the large door, he indicated two vacant chairs by the bookcase and took his place before the littered desk. When he had met the two women at the door, they had introduced themselves as Lolita Sergay and Edith Kaufmann.

"It's Lolita," said Mrs. Kaufmann. "She's ill."

Robert looked at the gaunt Spanish girl seated across

from him. He noticed deep circles under the nervous eyes which evaded his glance.

"But I am no medical doctor," Robert explained.

"Yes, yes, we know," said Mrs. Kaufmann.

Lolita Sergay did not speak coherently, but from what she said and Mrs. Kaufmann was able to tell him, it became clear to Robert at once that here was a girl near the breaking point and in dire need of medical help.

"It all started when Lolita was on tour a year ago," Edith Kaufmann continued. "Lolita was a concert singer —"

"I am sure Lolita is still a concert singer," Robert interrupted, looking toward the girl. Lolita gave a faint smile but continued to stare down at the rug before her.

"She contracted a bad throat while on tour with a troupe of Spanish singers last winter," Mrs. Kaufmann explained. "She was out sick for a night or two. I guess she began to get pretty worried about herself."

Mrs. Kaufmann explained that one of Lolita's colleagues came up to her one day and told her he knew where she could find something "that clears up the throat." Lolita had said she would try anything.

"What was it?" Robert asked.

"Dope," said Mrs. Kaufmann. "It was heroin."

Lolita began sobbing bitterly. She had been still up to now, but she could hold back the tears no longer.

"Lolita, darling," said Mrs. Kaufmann. "Don't be upset. This man is not a policeman. He's not even a doctor. He's a priest, and he wants to help you."

"God! It's no use!" Lolita screamed. "It's no use. I'm hooked. You don't know what it's like, you and your friend! I hate you for bringing me here! God, I hate you both!"

"Perhaps you had better step into the other room," said Robert.

Mrs. Kaufmann closed the door behind her.

Robert spent two grueling hours with the hysterical girl. He listened at length to Lolita as she shrieked and cursed and told her story over and over again. When he spoke, he spoke softly but firmly. He explained that he knew Lolita wanted to break her habit, but he said he knew she could not do it alone. It was going to take medical help, great will power, and prayer. Above all, he told her, it would require dependence on power beyond herself.

"You must really *desire* this cure," he explained. "This cannot be a halfhearted wish. And I think you will want to show God you're in earnest this time."

"Oh, I am! I am!" Lolita sobbed.

"Do you mean it enough to want to tell Him so?"

Lolita, at first surprised, said, "Yes, I do."

"Let us pray together."

For a few minutes, Mrs. Kaufmann, who had remained in the other room, could no longer hear the voices from Robert's study. Then she heard him say "Follow me," and saw the two of them go outside and around to the driveway.

Out there in the driveway Mrs. Kaufmann could hear Robert say something about showing she was in earnest this time. She could see a look of agony in the girl's face as Robert took a hammer and smashed what looked like tiny pellets.

About twenty minutes later, she and Lolita climbed into Robert's car, and the three of them drove to St. Joseph's Hospital, where Lolita reluctantly allowed herself to be led away.

Two days later when Robert went down the hospital hall, Lolita spotted him. Perspiration was pouring down her face.

"You put me in here!" she screamed, shaking her fist at him. Attendants tried to hold her quiet. "You talked me into giving you that goddamn needle and those pellets. And what did you do? Smashed them all in the driveway. I would kill you in a minute, if I could! God! I hate you so much I could wring your bloody neck!"

Robert spent some time with her. When he spoke, he again spoke softly. He did not lose his temper even when she cursed him in the vilest language at the top of her lungs.

"That was hard on you," said a nurse who followed Robert down the hall as he was leaving.

"Lolita is what counts, not how I feel," said Robert. "You and I have no idea what torture that poor girl is going through. She needs our prayers. I'm going to be praying for her, and I'm sure you will be, too."

Lolita's return to health took many months — much care, much will power, many prayers. But she did recover. Finally, one day, Lolita left a cryptic note of thanks by Robert's study door. She was leaving Kansas City, she explained, and was starting her new life in the East. Robert was never to hear of her again, but he knew full well that she was beginning the new life a whole person again.

Novels like *Babbitt* and *Arrowsmith* had already made the name of Sinclair Lewis a byword across the country when the author visited Kansas City in April of 1926. Mr. Lewis was preparing to write his novel *Elmer Gantry* and

had written Dr. Burris Jenkins, pastor of the Community
Christian Church in Kansas City, about the project. Since
the novel was to be built on the life of a Midwestern
clergyman, Dr. Jenkins invited the author to Kansas City.

On April 18, Dr. Jenkins invited Mr. Lewis to preach.
Crowds flocked to hear him. Mr. Lewis began his address
by referring to a newspaper article by a fundamentalist
who maintained that God had struck Luther Burbank dead
because of his work in behalf of science, which the fundamentalist felt contradicted the Bible.

Recalling the occasion, Charles Arthur Hawley later
wrote in the *Star*, "Lewis said the fundamentalist had the
wrong idea of God; that if he were right, God would strike
Lewis dead for what he was about to say in the next
fifteen minutes. He went on to say that God is greater than
man's concept of Him and he is an avenging God."

As he started his address, Mr. Lewis produced a watch
and placed it on the pulpit. At the end of the first fifteen
minutes, he picked up the watch and proudly told his
congregation, "The fifteen minutes are up, and I am still
alive!"

Newspapers across the country made much of the story,
as no doubt Mr. Lewis hoped would be the case.

That next week, the Reverend L. M. Birkhead, Pastor of
All Souls' Unitarian Church invited Robert to an all-clergy
luncheon for the noted author. About thirty clergymen
came out for the occasion.

After Dr. Birkhead formally introduced him, Mr. Lewis
explained at length that he was working on a novel about
a clergyman to be called *Elmer Gantry*, and that Dr.
Birkhead was "acting as advisor in matters ministerial,"

and that he hoped all of the gentlemen present would assist him in securing proper color for his hero. Elmer Gantry, the hero of the book, was an out-and-out fundamentalist who put extreme emphasis in his preaching on "salvation by the blood." To illustrate this point, Mr. Lewis took a napkin and held it up like a hymnal, then marched around the table, bellowing at the top of his lungs, "Saved by the blood! Saved by the blood!" His eyes were bulging from their sockets.

"What an ass!" said the man on Robert's left.

"Unconscious blasphemy, I think," Robert whispered. "But you must admit it's superb buffoonery. With that ability to pitch a hymn, he could have been a tent evangelist!"

"Elmer Gantry is a hypocrite," Lewis went on to say. "He's greedy. He's after filthy lucre. He's what St. Paul would call 'a lewd fellow of the baser sort.' Are there really any such in the ministry? I'm told that it is possible!"

A few days later, Lewis met with the clergy again.

"What can you ministers do that I can't do?" he asked.

"Preach," said a Baptist pastor.

"Not at all," said Lewis. "I preached at Dr. Burris Jenkins's church, and there was standing room only."

"He challenged God to strike him dead in fifteen minutes," someone whispered to Robert.

"Either God's timing was off, or Mr. Lewis's," Robert said to his companion.

After about three quarters of an hour, Robert excused himself to go to a funeral in the East Bottoms. He went quietly up to Mr. Lewis.

"I'm afraid I shall have to leave," Robert said softly.

"I have to go do something that perhaps you couldn't do. I have to go preach a funeral sermon for some sorrowing parents who have lost their little child."

"Why, I can do that!" Lewis chirped. "I preached my brother's funeral, and he stayed dead as long as the next one."

"But that's not the point," said Robert. "Those grief-stricken parents want assurance that their daughter *did not stay dead!* I want to tell them, in the name of the Child-lover, that their little daughter is playing in the nurseries of heaven. I believe that to be true. It may not be true, as you see it. But even if it were not true, Mr. Lewis, wouldn't it be a beautiful lie?"

Mr. Lewis stopped smirking. He rose from his chair, clasped Robert's hand, and said with great earnestness, "Spencer, the Prince of this world cometh and hath nothing in you."

A hush had fallen over the group. Robert walked quietly to the door.

CHAPTER XIX

Fire!

ON TUESDAY IN HOLY WEEK, Robert had gone to his study in the tower. Suddenly a woman rushed in to him, screaming hysterically, "Fire! There's a fire in the church!"

Robert ran to the nave. He could hear the roar of the flames. When he reached the door, he saw all the flags high over the side aisle whipping wildly, though there was not a breath of air outside.

Robert shouted at the sexton running toward him, "Have you sent in the alarm?"

"Yes, they'll be here in a minute."

By the time the firemen arrived, the interior of the great Norman structure was a blazing furnace.

The firemen began battling the flames at once.

The chief ran back to Robert. "Father," he said breathlessly, "we'll have to smash that big west window. The gas from those organ pipes may blow the roof off."

"Use your judgment," said Robert, "but if you have a fire in *your* Cathedral someday, I may break *your* windows."

Robert's heart sank. The Tiffany window dominated the whole west end of the church. It showed a hart beside a stream, to depict the passage from the Psalms: *As the hart panteth after the water brooks, so panteth my soul after thee, O God.* The window had been put in only a year before as a memorial to the Nelson family.

Robert heard the firemen smashing away the glass with their axes. In a moment the west window was gone, and the fire began to come under control.

Norman churches were built like fortresses. Grace and Holy Trinity, with its walls four feet thick, was no exception.

It's hard to burn such a church," said the fire chief. "I imagine that high trussed roof has only been scorched."

"It's ninety feet from the floor," said Robert.

"The altar seems to be intact," said someone.

Robert could see that it was, but the paintings of Gino Vinanzi were utterly ruined.

Gino, a gifted Italian painter, had done considerable work in churches throughout Italy. Robert had married him to a girl in the parish, and, on a visit to Kansas City, the artist had painted the three panels on the altar.

The fire was well under control by the time Amy arrived. "Oh, Robert," she said. "I just heard — I came at once." There was nothing she could say. She put her arms around him.

"Mr. Spencer," said the sexton. "Someone's at the door to see you."

Robert went out and found his friend Rabbi Samuel Mayerberg of the Temple B'Nai-Jehudah. The Rabbi clasped his hand.

"I know how great a blow this is," said he. "I am terribly sorry."

"Thank you, Sam."

"I just wanted you to know that you may use our temple for your services," he said, "and as long as you may need it."

"But, Sam," said Robert, "this is our Holy Week. There

would be Good Friday services. We'd be saying our old prayer for all Jews, infidels, and heretics, and I'm sure you would —"

"Never mind," said the Rabbi smiling. "The offer still stands, and we will gladly suit our own services to the convenience of yours."

Robert stood for a moment, looking into the eyes of his friend, "Sam, you are most kind," he said finally, "but I think we had better stay as close to the downtown area as we can. It's where we belong. Besides, if we move, people may say we're using the fire as an excuse to move to a more fashionable neighborhood."

"I mean it," Rabbi Mayerberg said again. "We should be proud to have you at the temple."

"Sam, I shall never forget your offer," said Robert.

Later that day, Robert arranged for the use of the near-by Masonic Temple for services until repairs to the church were finished.

The next morning word came back from the Tiffany studios that they still had the original drawings for the west window, and the vestry requested that the work of duplicating the destroyed window be started at once.

The Roanoke Baptist Church bulletin, the *Beacon*, carried the story, "Scarcely had the smoke cleared away before Rabbi Mayerberg of the B'Nai Jehudah Congregation called together the temple officers, the result being the offer of the synagogue to Grace and Holy Trinity until such time as the church should be restored." The article went on to state that Grace and Holy Trinity was doing a really Christlike service in Kansas City.

"And what are our Jewish brethren doing!" Robert exclaimed as he read the article.

At the Old Coates House, Archdeacon Watkins and a Jewish lawyer named Silverman joined Robert at lunch one day that week.

"Spencer," said the Archdeacon with a smile, "I think the Almighty burned Grace and Holy Trinity because of your sins."

Robert smiled. "I know I have enough of them to burn all the churches in Kansas City," he said, "but I don't agree with your theology. My own faith doesn't support the idea that God would burn the people's church because of the rector's sins. What do you think, Mr. Silverman?"

"Mr. Spencer," he said, "I don't believe the Almighty would even know a gentile church had burned!"

Robert laughed.

Many neighboring clergy had called to express concern and sympathy about the fire. "But it was Sam," Robert said over and over again, "it was Sam who offered first to help us!"

When at last the restored church was opened again, less than a year later, Robert made a point of inviting Sam Mayerberg to be one of the first guest speakers.

One evening when Robert came home, Kathleen asked her father, "Is it true?"

"Is what true?"

"Is it true you've invited a Rabbi to speak at the church?"

"Yes, it's true," said Robert. "I've asked Rabbi Mayerberg to speak next Sunday evening. Why do you ask?"

"I don't know, I'm just curious, that's all," said Kathleen.

"What's the matter? Is someone upset by my asking one

of our nation's great spiritual leaders to speak in our church?"

"Some of my friends said they thought it was funny for you to ask a Jew to speak," said Kathleen.

"Are *you* surprised, my dear?"

"Me surprised, Father?" said Kathleen. "Heavens, no! I know you too well. Besides, I agree with you about Rabbi Mayerberg. I think he's wonderful."

"He's always been a devoted friend of Grace and Holy Trinity," said Robert. "Remember what he did at the time of the fire?"

That Sunday evening, when Robert introduced the Rabbi, he said, "I consider him to be one of the best Christians I have ever known."

When Rabbi Mayerberg stood up to speak, he thanked Robert. "As your rector was introducing me, I was somewhat puzzled by his reference to me as a fine Christian," he said. "Then it flashed on me that he was using the term *Christian* in no dogmatic sense. To him the word connotes all that is good and true. It is a little like the story in Lessing's *Nathan the Wise* in which the Baron, grateful for a service Nathan had rendered him, exclaimed, 'By God, Nathan, thou art a Christian; never was a better! Soberly, Nathan replied, 'That which makes me a Christian makes thee to me a Jew.' Such sentiments on the part of my friends are a constant challenge to me to strive to become what they think and want to be."

Rabbi Mayerberg spoke brilliantly that evening. When Robert came home after the service, the telephone was ringing; it was the Senior Warden.

"I'll admit it," said the man. "I thought you were out

of your head to ask a Jewish Rabbi to speak to us. But I was all wrong. Rabbi Mayerberg said things tonight that I'll never forget. We must have him back."

Not long afterward, the compliment was returned, and Robert preached at the temple. He and Sam began to work together on a number of difficult civic crusades. Both men were to work hard getting the United Charities introduced throughout the city, and for improved housing and the like. Often such crusading demanded tireless speaking in machine and railroad shops, labor union meetings, lodges, schools, churches, or on the streets. Of course many other clergy and professional leaders did their part as well. It was to take several years to convert a whole city to its responsibilities to its homeless and helpless.

"Those men — that Rabbi and that Mr. Spencer — they're an eye-opening example to the rest of us," said one young man. "Guess it's the way they both see themselves as fellow servants in a great House."

But Robert little guessed that his days as rector of Grace and Holy Trinity were nearly over, or that a new chapter in his life was soon to begin.

CHAPTER XX

Rochet and Chimere

IN THE SPRING OF 1930, Bishop Sidney Catlin Partridge, gravely ill, sent word for Robert to come to see him. When Robert arrived at the Bishop's home, he was shown at once to the bedroom.

"Bon Pasteur," said the pale old man, "I'm afraid you'll have to preside at St. Joseph. The doctor was right — I know that now. I can't possibly stand the trip. You're senior presbyter. You are the one to take over at the Diocesan Convention."

Earlier that year, the Bishop had asked for the election of a bishop coadjutor to assist him with the missions and smaller parishes of this diocese. "We are really choosing Bishop Partridge's successor," Robert told Amy that night. "I hate to think about it, Amy, but I'm afraid we're going to be without him soon."

"Oh, don't even say it," said Amy. "Maybe with the assistance of another bishop he'll manage. Whom do you think they ought to elect?"

"I'd like to see a man like George Davidson," said Robert.

"Your friend in Los Angeles?"

"Yes. I think he's the type of man they need," said Robert.

At lunch the next Thursday, a group of laymen and

clergy got on the subject of the election. Robert again brought up the name of his friend.

"George is an able man and has done a fine job with that great church of his — St. John's — out in Los Angeles," said Robert. "He was born in Kansas City. He knows the diocese. I think he'd make a great bishop."

"He would," said the Chancellor. "George is a grand person. Why, I've known him since he was a boy."

"Mr. Spencer," said George Mansgrove, "I think you are going to be nominated. Everyone knows you. You're rector of a big church."

Robert smiled. "I don't think so. Oh, sure, I may have a token nomination. Chances are, there will be a lot of those."

The day for the convention came. Amy and Kathleen drove up to St. Joseph with Robert.

"For someone who said he dreaded presiding," Kathleen whispered to her mother, "Father seems calm." Her mother agreed.

At last came the time for the election. Many names were put in nomination: Benjamin Washburn, "able broad Churchman" who had just recently left Kansas City for Emmanuel Church, Boston; James Pernette De Wolfe, "intense young Anglo-Catholic" rector of St. Andrew's, Kansas City; and many others.

"I nominate Robert Nelson Spencer," said a voice finally.

One of the lay delegates, a newspaperman, stood up. "This young man looks too bilious to me to be a bishop," he said in a loud voice. "Bishops always look vigorous. Why, just look at him! He's thin and haggard-looking. I haven't anything against his character, but I don't honestly think he could stand the strain."

"Bilious!" roared Henry B. Ashley, a prominent lawyer-delegate, jumping to his feet. "He has been bilious enough to work on a road-building gang in Kansas City, bilious enough to run a shelter for migratory workers and a sanitarium for meningitis victims, bilious enough to travel around preaching long missions, bilious enough to work a round-the-clock seven-day week, helping all sorts of civic causes, visiting the sick, crusading for better housing, and so on! He's been bilious enough to do all this for his Lord! No sir, I don't agree with you. I think Robert Nelson Spencer would make an excellent bishop, one we could be proud of!"

The balloting followed several more hot debates. About an hour later, the election was over. Robert had won. He looked stunned. Amy looked at him as people rushed forward to congratulate him. "My bilious Robert," she said to Kathleen softly — "they really love him!"

The Spencers drove back to Kansas City, and Robert went to see Bishop Partridge at once. When he went in and told the old man, Bishop Partridge beamed. "Thank God!" he said. "Bon Pasteur, I hoped you'd be elected, but of course I couldn't say so. I am very happy, very happy."

He paused, then straightened himself up on the pillows. "I know you will accept your election."

"But I don't think I can," said Robert. "I'm not even sure I should. I like my work at Grace and Holy Trinity. It's the sort of —"

Bishop Partridge held up his hand. "Don't make up your mind now. Just go home and pray about it. Then come to see me tomorrow."

That evening at dinner, the family ate in silence; then

Robert excused himself and went to his study. Amy said nothing. She knew what a tormenting decision Robert faced. He did not wish to leave his friends and his work at Grace and Holy Trinity. He had married those people, baptized their babies, buried members of their families.

"When you have shared in such moments," Robert used to say, "a part of your heart stays with those people."

No, Robert had no desire to leave, but his bishop was trying hard to influence him to do so.

Alone in his study Robert prayed and thought for some time. As the evening wore on, he tried reading some of the Epistles of Saint Paul from the Bible on his desk. What shameless confessions they were! Paul was torn apart by internal conflict. He said he did the things he hated and what he would do he could not do. Was this an easy ministry? Did he stay on in places he liked? He felt compelled to go many places and endure countless hardships before he was able to say with justifiable pride at the end, "I have fought a good fight; I bear in my body the marks of the Lord Jesus."

Robert spent a restless night, then returned the next morning to the Bishop's house to tell him he was still not sure what he should do. Again Bishop Partridge told him to go home and pray about it.

"I believe it is the will of God and not for you to dismiss this election lightly," he said.

On his desk when he returned home, Robert found part of an article "What Is a Bishop?" which Amy had torn from some periodical:

The Bishop must be a man of affairs and many affairs. He is expected to fulfill many functions. He is . . . a businessman, and an administrator and an executive. Particularly is he the trouble man of a large corporation. All the church quarrels gather about his devoted head. He has the responsibility for everything that goes wrong, often without the authority to set anything right. He serves as a lightning rod to carry off the accumulated wrath of the ecclesiastical heavens. He is constantly called upon to act as a judge and should have a judicial temperament. He is also a traveling man, a kind of ecclesiastical drummer or salesman. He is even sometimes in demand as a social ornament to say grace at banquets, make after-dinner speeches, adorn the stage at public meetings, and minister to the aesthetic needs of conventional society at fashionable weddings, baptisms, and funerals. In the midst of all this distraction and dissipation he is expected to find time and mind to be a preacher and a teacher, a scholar and a leader, and above all, a man of prayer and a man of God.

The next day, Robert read the article to Bishop Partridge and said, "But I couldn't be all those things!"

"Of course you couldn't. You wouldn't have to be," said the Bishop. "I think that article is a bit glib and cynical."

"And besides, Bishop," Robert continued, "I don't want to go any higher."

The old man looked at Robert with searching eyes. "Bon Pasteur," he said, "it is not for you or me to call the signals. This is not a question of whether you want to go any higher; it is a question of whether our Lord wishes you to do so. Don't you know that our calling to do God's will may often sweep us into new work, even into work we do not want to do? But I can't talk any more. Come back tomorrow," he said and fell back dramatically on his pillow with a deliberate groan.

When Robert returned the next day, Bishop Partridge could see that the look of distress had gone from his face. "I have made my decision, Bishop," Robert said as he entered the room. "I have decided I must accept."

Bishop Partridge smiled. "Bon Pasteur," he said, "kneel down. I want to say a prayer of thanksgiving and give you my blessing."

As Robert left the house, he met the newspaperman who had thought him too bilious.

"Have you reached a decision?" he asked Robert.

"I have. I am going to accept."

"I'm really glad," said the man. "Since the convention, I've talked with scores of people. They are behind you 100 per cent."

A few weeks later, Bishop Partridge died; when the day came for Robert's consecration he would therefore become Bishop of the Diocese of West Missouri. The ceremony took place at Grace and Holy Trinity on Tuesday, October 28, 1930. All summer, elaborate preparations were made for the service, so that everything would go smoothly. The canons of the Church, first of all, require a majority of consents from the other bishops of the Episcopal Church and a majority of the Standing Committees composed of clergy and laymen. Canon law also requires that at least three bishops shall lay their hands upon the head of the priest who is to be made a bishop. Normally, one of the three is the Presiding Bishop, but due to a conflict in dates, as another man was being consecrated in New York, the Presiding Bishop could not come to the Midwestern ceremony. In his place Bishop Capers of West Texas acted as consecrator.

When the Spencers reached the church, a man met them at the door with a large chart showing where each clergyman was to go to put on his vestments. Amy followed Robert to the sacristy to make certain he had everything he needed.

"It's a long time since I first looked after your vestments in Junction City," she said, looking into his eyes. Robert looked back at her tenderly, thinking of the happy way they had come together.

"You and Kathleen had better go take your places," he said as he stood at the door, dressed in his long purple cassock for the first time.

Just then, one of the parish secretaries rushed into the sacristy with a stack of papers. "Telegrams," she explained breathlessly.

Robert did not have time to read them all, but a quick glance showed him that the messages bore familiar names: Father Houghton from the Scranton days, Dr. Fred O'Donnell from Junction City, friends from Ludington. The Presiding Bishop wired: AT CONSECRATION IN NEW YORK CATHEDRAL MY THOUGHTS WILL FOLLOW YOU AND MY PRAYERS THAT YOU MAY BE STRENGTHENED AND GUIDED BY THE HOLY SPIRIT AND BLESSED IN ALL YOUR WORK.

"Did you see the bulletin board in front of the Temple B'Nai Jehudah?" someone asked Robert. "Rabbi Mayerberg has listed his sermon topic for Friday night as: ROBERT NELSON SPENCER — MAN OF GOD."

"Did Sam really do that?" asked Robert, shaking his head with pleasure.

At last, the hour arrived. Mrs. Billings, the organist, finished playing the last of the pre-service selections. Acolytes finished lighting the tall candles in the sanctuary. The tremendous procession filed out the door and around the block. Crowds lined the curb to watch. First came the crucifer, followed by the choir and vestry of Grace and Holy Trinity. Next came the second crucifer, followed by the directors of St. Luke's Hospital, lay members of the

Executive Council, the Chancellor, lay members of the Standing Committee, followed by the entire clergy of the diocese.

Robert watched the procession as it made its way up the walk into the church. He watched the third crucifer, followed by the bearers of testimonials, deputy registrar, acolytes, various visiting bishops, bishops with testimonials, the litanist, masters of ceremonies. Then Robert swung into line, still in his purple cassock and rochet of white linen. Two priests flanked him, and behind him came the presenting bishops, the preacher, co-consecrators.

As Robert had entered the door of the church for the consecration service, he had heard the choir and congregation singing "Ancient of Days, Who sittest, throned in glory." The author's name appeared on the program: It was William Crosswell Doane, the late Bishop of Albany, who on that snowy Christmas morning, long ago, had closed the door on young Robert.

In the moments which followed twelve bishops laid their hands on Robert's head; he was clothed in the full vestments; and Bishop Cook of Delaware, concluding the consecration sermon, addressed Robert formally as "Brother" for the first time. That day, Robert became officially "The Right Reverend Robert Nelson Spencer, Bishop of the Diocese of West Missouri."

"What is your program to be?" asked reporters when the ceremony was over.

"Gentlemen of the press," said the new Bishop solemnly, "My program is quite simple. I hope to help make the Episcopalians of West Missouri Christians."

CHAPTER XXI

Member of the Wedding

WHEN BISHOP COOK PREACHED at Robert's consecration service, he had reminded the congregation that a bishop must be a true pastor to his own clergy.

Robert took the Bishop's words to heart. When he and Amy set out to find a house, they agreed that it would have to be large enough to house all the clergy of the diocese, if necessary, because Robert had his heart set on at least one "open house" or retreat for his clergy a year.

When at last they chose 610 East Forty-Seventh Street, Robert told Amy, "This will be more than adequate for the annual clergy retreat. We can turn the large second floor porch into a dormitory for the men from out of town."

"We can borrow cots from the hospital," said Amy.

Accordingly, in the fall, Robert invited all his men to Kansas City — about twenty-two in all. On the first day, Robert conducted a business session to go over diocesan plans for the coming winter. Then on the second, he led his clergy in a "quiet day" of retreat and meditation.

Amy and Kathleen, who had moved to a neighbor's for the night, returned to the house to help prepare meals. Otherwise, Robert was alone with the priests, who now looked to him as their pastor — a sobering responsibility Robert prayed he would be able to meet effectively.

Dear God, give me grace — he thought — not to be

long-winded, to listen as well as to speak, and in all things to do Thy will, not my own.

That winter the new Bishop visited Binghamton, where local papers had made much of the Tunnel "farmboy and station helper now a bishop."

One local rector came up to Robert during his visit. "How did you do it?" he asked. "You were crippled in your youth. You had no education until you were a grown man. And you were born — of all places — in Tunnel, one of the smallest towns in America! How on earth did you ever become a bishop?"

Robert smiled. "I guess Saint Paul would tell you 'This thing is a mystery.' As for my being born in Tunnel, I don't think it fair to speak disparagingly of the little Nazareths of Central New York. Why, we *all* came from a biological tunnel to begin with, and you know it! But forgive me — I have a train to catch."

A record-breaking snowstorm delayed his train. Robert was very late for a meeting in the Midwest he had been asked to address. When finally he did arrive, he shook the snow from his overcoat, quickly put on his vestments and went out into the church and up into the pulpit.

"I am sorry to have been delayed by the blizzard," he said smiling. "I take my text from the Gospel according to St. Mark: *And pray ye that your flight be not in the winter.*"

The congregation howled.

In May of 1931 Robert returned to Dickinson College to receive an honorary degree at the 148th Commencement Exercises at Carlisle, Pennsylvania. Honorary degrees went to eight men, among them Supreme Court

Justice Owen J. Roberts, who gave the Commencement Address, and Bishop James Edward Freeman of Washington, who preached the Baccalaureate Sermon.

When Robert, dressed in his black academic gown, stepped forward to receive his Doctor of Divinity degree, President Morgan hailed him as "A son of the College, a devoted minister of the Gospel and devoted to its truth; a hater of shams and skillful in exposing them with rapier-like thrusts; recognized by your great Church and called to Episcopal leadership . . ."

A bishop's vestments consist of a purple cassock; over this a fair linen rochet, or coat-line garment with cuffs and bands on the sleeves; a floor-length chimere of black, sometimes red, silk or satin with armholes like a vest. Some bishops wear a cope and miter. Copes are made of heavy, richly embroidered brocades in various colors. Miters are made usually of matching material and have two ribbonlike strands which hang down in back. Robert wore a cope and miter on occasion, but found them difficult to carry around his diocese of thirty-seven thousand square miles. "It's like carting a grand piano and bench with you!" he said, and so he usually carried with him only the less elaborate cassock, rochet, and chimere on his visitations. When some overzealous Altar Guild lady complained to him, "But Bishop, your vestments look wrinkled!" more than once he smiled and said that he wondered how Saint Paul looked as Bishop on his first appointment, after he had been immersed a night and a day in the sea. Robert said he could not seem to convince himself that a few wrinkles would necessarily obstruct the channels of grace.

As he told the Diocesan Women's Auxiliary one day in an address: "Something is lacking in me — and I deplore it — of that vehement insistence on vesture, that decency and order that makes up the perfectly regulated Sanctuary and Service. So much of that do I lack that I am often embarrassed by what seems to me to be overattention, but which is, of course, as things should be. I'm like the old woman in a mountain cabin who told David Starr Jordan, 'Mr. Jordan, poor people have poor ways!' "

"Thank you for saying that! Thank you for saying what you did," said fluttery Mrs. Barbieri.

"Not at all," said Robert, "I meant it. I am afraid I'm not as tolerant as I should be. I'm afraid I have little use for those people, who are often otherwise intelligent and even saintly, who seem to drool over nomenclature as if such titles were as important as the Name that is above every name."

Clarence Darrow was a brilliant lawyer. Few die-hards denied it. He had a penchant, it was said, for going out of his way to plead the case of unpopular persons and causes, but even his arch-critics seemed to admire the man's "word wizardry" and the agility of his mind in court. His defense of Loeb and Leopold and his defense of John T. Scopes in the so-called "Monkey Trial" won Clarence Darrow banner headlines across the country.

Through the years, in off-the-cuff comments, Darrow showed little sympathy for religion. When someone pointed out that financial depressions drew people to the Church, he quipped, "So do funerals." "Don't you believe in anything?" one person asked him. "I used to believe in blondes," he replied.

When Darrow came to Kansas City, during Robert's early years as bishop, his hostess there invited Robert to lunch to meet him.

"I rather dread this," he told Amy as he left the house. "They tell me Darrow not only doesn't like clergy — he sometimes eats them!"

When Robert arrived, Darrow was standing before the fireplace. His hair was uncombed, and his suit looked as if it had not been off his back for a week. As Robert entered the room, Darrow stared at him up and down like a prosecuting attorney.

"I am delighted to meet you, Mr. Darrow," Robert said. "I have followed your career with interest and read a number of things you have written."

"Thank you," said Darrow crisply.

"This may surprise you, sir," said Robert, "but I think your *Farmington* is the best thing you have written to date."

"*Farmington!*" Darrow's face lighted up. "I wrote that anonymously. How did you know —"

"And I think you were writing that book to draw a picture of every man's boyhood," Robert continued. "In a way every man reading it should detect familiar strains from his own experience."

"Quite right," said Darrow. "My hat is off to you for being so astute."

Later on, at luncheon, Robert turned to Darrow. "You're a lawyer for the underdog, aren't you?" he asked smiling.

"People say that I am," said Darrow. "But why do you ask?"

"Because I happen to work for Someone who has you beat a thousand miles as a lawyer for the underdog."

"Who is that?" Darrow asked.

"Jesus Christ," said Robert.

Mr. Darrow did not smile, even with his eyes. "Yes," he said soberly, "you are right."

Robert continued, "You know the saying of John 'If any man sin, we have an Advocate with the Father' means exactly what it says. It means that our Lord is indeed an attorney — and an attorney for the defense, Mr. Darrow. He is never a prosecuting attorney."

Mr. Darrow smiled. "I've never heard it put that way before."

"Even His credentials say so. 'God sent not his Son into the world to condemn the world; but that the world through him might be saved.' "

"What kind of cases would you say your Lawyer took?" asked Darrow.

"Many kinds," said Robert. "There was the case of the woman who was being dragged through the streets. It was a difficult case. The law was plain and the evidence undoubted and the penalty prescribed. Yet He got her off.

"Or take the case of the woman versus Sychar," Robert continued. "That woman met the Lawyer at a well. She was a woman of known evil character, and yet Jesus took her case. The Lawyer began to probe her story. She tried to evade. She argued their political differences. She questioned the depth of the well. She even tried to get the Lawyer into a theological argument as to whether a Samaritan mountain or a Jerusalem temple was the more fit place to worship God. But the Lawyer would not let her go — for her own sake."

Darrow looked at his hostess, then back at Robert. "But do go on," he said smiling. "I'm interested."

"Each time Jesus said, in effect, " 'Before I take your case, I must have your whole story, all the facts. If you are innocent, I want to know it. If you are guilty, I want to know that. You see, if I am to make an intelligent defense of you, you must tell me everything.'"

Mr. Darrow turned to the hostess. "You know, if I weren't so old, I honestly think this man could make an Episcopalian of me!" he said.

"I wouldn't take the trouble," said Robert. "What's important is the fact that you are always for the underdog like that Lawyer Himself."

As Robert stood up to leave, he added, "You know, I think Newman was right the time he said that often our denominational bickerings are like a dogfight in a flower bed: they settle nothing but the flowers!"

One morning Kathleen came down to breakfast, beaming.

"You certainly look cheery this morning," said her mother, as she poured the coffee.

"Why shouldn't I?" Kathleen asked.

"Did you have a good time last night?" Robert asked.

"Yes, Father, a wonderful time. I went on a blind date with a boy named Louis DeYong."

"You got home pretty late, too," her mother said.

"I guess I did, Mother," said Kathleen. "It *must* have been pretty late."

"What's this Louis DeYong like?" Amy asked.

"Oh, he's wonderful, Mother — I don't know how to describe him exactly. We had lots of fun. We had so much in common, I thought we'd never stop talking. We got to talking and talked for hours. I haven't an idea what time I got home."

"What does this boy do?" Amy asked.

"He's with the Telephone Company." Kathleen turned to her father. "You know, it's funny about my hunches, but I have a feeling he's going to ask me to marry him."

"Marry him!" Amy exclaimed. "You only met him last night!"

"Yes, I know," said Kathleen, "but — well, Dee's different."

"You mother's right," said Robert. "This is ridiculous talk. You hardly know the boy." He went over to the mantel, took down a pipe, lighted it, and disappeared into his study with a copy of the morning paper.

That week, Kathleen brought Dee around to the house to meet her parents. They liked the young man tremendously.

"I feel better about the whole thing," said Robert, smiling.

"He's a dear," Amy agreed.

Within three weeks, Kathleen and Dee became engaged. Robert, who was down in Springfield when the news broke, sent a wire to the engagement dinner: KAY HAS LEARNED HER ABC. NOW GO ON AND LEARN YOUR DEE. DEE IS FURTHER ON THE WAY. HE HAS NOW ARRIVED AT KAY. MY NUMBER IS GRAND OH OH OH OH — DAD.

When Robert returned to Kansas City, he found Amy in a dither over wedding plans. The quick engagement, to be sure, had taken everyone's breath away. "But Kathleen is grown up," Amy reminded her husband late that evening. "It's her life, and Dee is her choice. You said yourself you liked him. He seems to have both feet on the ground and to be really crazy about Kathleen."

"He seems ambitious, too," said Robert.

The very thought of the wedding terrified Amy when she considered what they would have to do to get ready. February 3 was to be the date. Since Robert was Bishop, care had to be taken that feelings were not hurt.

"An evening wedding is planned," said the paper, "at Grace and Holy Trinity, the Bishop's old church" — now officially the Cathedral of the Diocese.

The Spencers sent invitations not only to friends in Kansas City but to every priest in the Diocese as well, with word that the invitation should be read from each pulpit three weeks before the wedding. "We want the whole diocesan family to feel included," Kathleen explained.

When at last the day of the wedding arrived, the Altar Guild decorated the Cathedral for the occasion. Easter lilies and white snapdragons filled the altar vases. The center aisle was lined with candles, lilies, and smilax.

As luck would have it, Kansas City that day had what reportedly was the worst ice storm in years.

"Amy, I've just been out," said Robert. "The streets are a solid sheet of ice. Driving will be hazardous."

Amy went to the window. "We'll be lucky to have a corporal's guard show up."

Robert arrived early and looked in at the Cathedral. Already a good number of people had arrived. Mrs. Billings, who had prepared an elaborate organ program for before the service, was playing the Franck *Chorale in B Minor*.

"Are you giving her away, Bishop?" asked the sexton. "Or are you conducting the service?"

"The service," said Robert as he hurried back to put on his vestments.

Finally, the big moment came. Guests were standing

two deep against the walls on each side of the packed Cathedral.

The choir, singing the Bridal Chorus from *Lohengrin,* preceded the wedding party up the aisle. Amy's brother, Kensmuire Gordon Moffatt, gave Kathleen away.

A hush fell over the candlelit Cathedral as Robert, dressed in the brilliant red chimere he reserved for special occasions, pronounced Kathleen and Dee man and wife "in the Name of the Father, and of the Son, and of the Holy Ghost."

After a reception at the Spencers' home, Dee and his bride rushed through a blizzard of rice to a waiting car.

"Cheer up!" Amy whispered in her husband's ear. "She's not leaving our lives. I know she's not."

Robert just stood there watching the car disappear. For a moment he could not speak.

CHAPTER XXII

"Père Marquette"

INDEED THE MARRIAGE did not break up the family; it merely made a foursome of the Spencers.

"We are all devoted to Dee," Amy wrote to friends in Ludington. "He and Kathleen live only a few miles from us, and the three of us often go with Robert on his trips around the Diocese to St. Joseph, Sedalia, Independence, Carthage, or wherever he has to go. Robert encourages us to go with him. He says he thinks the people like to know the Bishop's family better. Of course, Dee is a big help on the driving. He and Robert seem to hit it off famously."

As the Bishop, Robert was much in demand as a preacher all over the country. Amy said it seemed to her as if she were forever packing or unpacking a suitcase for her husband. He did considerable traveling outside the Diocese as well as around his own West Missouri — for the National Preaching Mission, the Bishops' Crusade, perhaps a local preaching mission in Santa Rosa, California, or Lenten addresses at St. Bartholomew's in New York City.

On one occasion, Robert had gone to St. Paul, Minnesota. He was about to enter the church for the start of an evening service. The choir had already started up the aisle when he got the message that there was an urgent long-distance call for him.

Robert hurried to the phone. It was Dee.

"The baby is here," said Dee. "You have a grand-daughter, Amy Elsa DeYong. Kathleen is fine and sends her love."

Robert hurried back to the nave and up the aisle. When he reached the altar, he turned to the congregation.

"I am sorry to be late," he said huskily, "but I have just received word that I have become a grandfather." He opened his prayer book. "Let my prayer be set forth in thy sight as the incense," he read; "and let the lifting up of my hands be an evening sacrifice."

When, one evening a few weeks later, Amy and Robert were taking care of their granddaughter so that Kathleen and Dee could get out, the baby became fretful. Robert picked her up and walked back and forth across the living room.

"And what on earth do you think you're doing with that child?" Amy asked.

"Hush! It's colic," said Robert pacing the length of the room. "We're slog . . . slog . . . slogging over Africa!"

"I'm not sure she has colic," said Amy, laughing, "but she certainly likes to slog over Africa and you are without doubt the silliest grandfather that ever lived."

The local Greek Orthodox Pastor invited Robert to preach at a special service that winter because the Greek Bishop was unable to come. Robert said he was flattered and accepted.

When the day came, Robert appeared at the church early to make certain he knew what the Greek Pastor expected him to do.

As the service got under way, the Pastor let Robert into the dimly candlelit sanctuary and nodded to him to take his place on the Bishop's throne. In the semidarkness Robert sat down by mistake on the large footpace. Robert heard a faint ripple of laughter from the congregation. The priest came over and whispered to him to move up to the large seat behind him.

"You're sitting on the stool!" the Pastor whispered.

When Robert climbed up into the pulpit to preach, he announced, "I have decided to change my sermon text to the Fourteenth Chapter of the Gospel according to St. Luke beginning at the tenth verse: *When thou art bidden . . . to a wedding . . . go and sit down in the lowest room; that when he that bade thee cometh, he may say unto thee, Friend, go up higher.*"

Robert looked down at the congregation before him. "This text," he said smiling, "by your countryman Saint Luke the Evangelist, is today fulfilled in your eyes. For you saw what happened. You saw me sit on the stool and saw your pastor ask me to move up. To me, you see, this service is a kind of wedding between your ancient faith and my own."

That evening, the doorbell rang, and the bearded Greek Pastor entered the living room all smiles.

"Your Beatitude," he said "my congregation sent me to thank you for your humor today. Our bishops are as solemn as owls, but you were delightful."

Then he handed Robert a large wheaten Host and a Greek New Testament which had been blessed by the Patriarch. A wheaten Host is a large wafer, about the size of a butterplate; it is not for consumption but kept as a sort of reserve ikon.

In a few moments, the priest was off again.

"Didn't he have a spiritual face?" asked Amy.

"Yes, he did," said Robert. "He was light-bearded like so many portraits of the young Christ and had a real twinkle in those luminous eyes of his."

Kathleen rushed in the front door. "Father!" she cried. "To think that you of all people didn't know any better than to sit on the floor in that Greek church! I'm ashamed of you. . . . Here, Mother, I brought you some flowers."

Relaxing up at Ludington the summer of 1934, Robert wrote light verse which he called *Sermons in Shorts*. Each poem, inspired by a Bible verse, consisted of two or three appropriate quatrains. For instance, one rainy afternoon inspired the piece:

RAIN AND UMBRELLAS
He sendeth rain on the just and on the unjust.
— ST. MATTHEW V:45.
> Upon this text of falling rain
> An ancient bishop doting,
> Pronounced our economy "all wet" —
> His reasons I am quoting:

> "By Heaven's law," said he, "the rain
> Falls on the just and unjust fellas;
> But mostly on the just, because
> The unjust have the just's umbrellas."

At Ludington, Robert was able, also, to pursue another interest. From the time he was a boy in Tunnel, Robert had been interested in the life of Père Marquette — ever since his mother had read him accounts of the Father's adventures in Prescott's histories. In the library at Cleveland, Robert had seen *The Jesuit Relations,* seventy volumes of diaries which were sent back to France in the early days as records of the Jesuit work in the United States and Canada. Robert saw how Marquette figured in those diaries. "They make rather heavy reading," he said afterward. "You have to wade through maybe a hundred pages or so before you come across something about the man." Up at Ludington, Robert found only one book about Marquette in the local library, and whenever Marquette was portrayed in local amateur theatricals, the actors inevitably made him a sort of comic character.

"It's all wrong," said Robert. "After all, we should revere the man. Didn't he choose to die here? Why, that alone should make Ludington famous. I think we should do something to commemorate the man — not make fun of him."

Robert discussed the idea of a Marquette memorial with Bishop Quayle. "We might even stage a great outdoor pageant," he told his neighbor, Mr. Stearns. The Chamber of Commerce asked Robert to give an address on Marquette.

Back at the cottage, Robert told Amy. "Instead of a speech, I think I'll try writing a pageant myself."

"How can you?" Amy asked. "You're a thousand miles from your books." She stopped a minute and stared at her husband. "You're not planning to go back to Kansas City, I hope," she said. "I won't let you. You're up here for a rest."

All that week up at the lake, it rained; and Robert, with only the one book, a few random notes, and his memory to guide him, worked hour after hour until the pageant script was finally completed.

He took his manuscript into the living room and read it aloud to the family.

"Is it all right, do you think?" he asked when he had finished.

"Robert," said Amy soberly, "it's the greatest thing you have ever done."

Robert took the text over to Mr. Stearns.

"You must let the others hear this," he said. "It's great!"

Robert read it that evening to a group of Ludington friends.

"Everyone seems enthusiastic," he told Amy when he got home. "They want to stage a pageant and make a great production of it."

"I know, I heard," said Amy. "Florence told me a few minutes ago about the professional producing firm they're planning to get to put it on."

In a few days the professional director came down, and examined Robert's text in detail.

"This can be tremendous," he told Robert and the members of the pageant committee.

Tryouts for parts in the pageant the next spring brought out people from all around the Ludington area. Much publicized rehearsals were begun, and Amy and Robert went out to see the production take shape. Several hundred people were taking part.

"I think that chorus of girls in blue robes should be wonderfully effective," said Amy after the dress rehearsals.

"They're supposed to dramatize the idea of Marquette going down the Mississippi," remarked Robert. "How did you like the Indian dances?"

"Fine," said Amy, "but how did they get so many real Indians?"

"I don't know," answered her husband, "but they have been most cooperative."

At last the time for the first performance arrived: August 9, 1935. The pageant was to be performed out of doors and was drawing a tremendous crowd. Robert would be the narrator and read his poem from the specially built high wooden pulpit.

At last Robert appeared, in his long purple cassock, mounted the steps to the pulpit, and stood up, high above the audience, silhouetted against the August sky.

Slowly, in his resonant voice, he began to read the opening words of his script:

> Kinsmen, tonight in mimic action on our stage,
> And by the aid of pageantry, we seek to part
> History's tangled thicket of three hundred years
> And show you a man, halting for one brief night
> Upon this shore — halting that he might die in peace,
> Out of the wind's and the water's way . . .
> Yet made this spot in Ludington's sands
> A shrine in history, for all coming time,
> A memory for libraries, and a tale of heroism
> to be told at firesides . . .

The pageant continued. Robert told of how Marquette, with the honors of French universities thick upon him and with the honors of the Roman Church his for the accepting, put all that behind him and at the age of twenty-nine set sail for what was then "darkest America." The pageant told how he gave the world its first authentic knowledge of the Mississippi. He measured nearly three thousand miles in paddle strokes on lakes and rivers. Pilots, said the narrator, still navigate on soundings Marquette made nearly three hundred years ago.

Kathleen saw that her mother's eyes were moist when Robert read the account of Marquette's death at Ludington.

"I was right that day in the cottage," Amy whispered. "It is very moving, isn't it?"

Kathleen nodded.

Robert continued:

> It is Spring in Ludington —
> Spring in midmost May, in 1675; Spring
> That loosed Winter's grip upon the river
> And sent it singing by a low hill
> Into the great Inland Sea.
> The two French voyagers who had paddled
> His canoe — which was now his ambulance —
> Tenderly carried his frail body up the hill
> And made a shelter and built a fire,
> For the May night was chill . . .
> He was thirty-eight when he died
> That May night in 1675. But his brave heart
> Had beaten too fast, and he had to go home
> Before it was noon!
> Listen, Kinsmen, to his last words.
> They were spoken slowly and softly,
> As though he whispered in another world . . .
> "My soul . . . hangs . . . upon his Word. Jesu! Mari!"
> And the gates of Heaven lifted above what is now
>   Ludington
> And the light of the Eternal City fell fair
> Upon his face.
> We shall build his monument here . . . and,
> Far away his monument shall be,
> In the dark lands he opened to the Light:
> On sun-drenched Lake; in the half-Arctic night,
> And his great River, winding to the sea.

The pageant won Robert wide acclaim. The text was published at once locally, then later reprinted for distribution to some sixty thousand school children in Michigan.

Pope Pius XI, hearing of the pageant, directed that a letter of commendation be sent.

It is the fervent prayer of His Holiness [the letter said in part] that success may attend the pageant and that the favor of God may richly recompense all those who have contributed to make better known and appreciated one whose character and ideals may well serve as an inspiring example to men and women of our own day.

"Quite an honor for an Episcopalian!" said the Roman Catholic Bishop of Grand Rapids who, with other dignitaries of the Church, witnessed the pageant.

In 1936, Robert took part in a much publicized National Preaching Mission across the country. The objective of the crusade, it was explained, was not to promote Protestantism but rather "to fight irreligion on all fronts." Traveling with noted preachers like Ivan Lee Holt and E. Stanley Jones, Robert and his colleagues called for laymen and clergy alike to rise up and take a stand for their faith out where they lived and worked.

In one of his addresses, Robert summed up the urgency of the times by saying: "A friend in East London told me that she had been sitting with a woman in a mean little room, a miserable hovel it was, and in her arms lay a delirious child. The mother was trying to comfort the child, who kept screaming into the mother's face, 'Mother, Mother!' The child looked up with unseeing, wild feverish eyes into the mother's eyes. 'Yes, darling, Mother is here. This is Mother.' But the child still screamed on. My friends, out there our sick world is lying in the very arms of God and does not know it!"

More and more, Robert's voice was heard in the national

Church. "What do *you* think of the idea of an American missal to replace the Book of Common Prayer?" one reporter asked him.

"Gentlemen of the press," he replied, "let the Bishop who is without sin cast the first missal!"

Then he added, "But I do feel there is a need for additional prayers. It is terribly embarrassing to go up and open an altar prayer book and let loose a veritable shower of Dr. Orchard's prayers."

Dr. Orchard, a famous British preacher, had written numerous published prayers which were widely used in local churches both here and abroad.

When Robert was in Tulsa for a preaching mission, reporters asked him, "What is your Church's view of the marriage of the Duchess of Windsor and the Duke?"

His face reddened. "This sort of thing makes me angry," he said. "Here we come on a great preaching mission to try to evangelize America, and you come asking a question like that! Well, since you ask, I'd say that you yourself ought to know without my telling you that no woman can discard two jacks and draw a royal flush, which is what the Duchess of Windsor has tried to do."

Robert was embarrassed the next morning to see his remark about the Windsors quoted in newspaper headlines. "Why do they stress the unimportant?" he said.

In the busy weeks that followed, he gave many talks before audiences all across the Midwest.

To a convention of school principals, he said, "There is a twist in human nature that makes us revile the generation in which we live and claim we have no leaders, no opportunities. I say there *are* giants in the land today, although Man lives too close to recognize them oftentimes

and single them out. But would it not be better to pray —
not that there be giants but rather that God should make
us tall?"

Addressing another group, he declared, "One can use
the newspaper as a means of grace, a kind of prayer book.
To read of motor accidents, of a mother burned by gasoline
while making a living for her brood, of 'battle, murder, and
sudden death,' of 'sinking ships and praying hands' — to
read of such things and not believe, to believe and not
care, that is terrible. But to read, and to breathe a sentence
of prayer for one's unfortunate brothers and sisters, this is
to make even the newspaper a litany and a means of
grace."

Addressing a large service organization Robert said,
"What did our Lord do? He saw that men, like coins, were
stamped with His image, and He set out to reclaim those
who had dropped from circulation. 'Peace' and 'good
will'? They are like two halves of a round-trip ticket, *not
good if detached!*"

After a Corporate Communion Breakfast, a young boy
asked him, "You never say very much about the Devil.
Why is that?"

Robert smiled. "I prefer to speak of the Devil as the
Great Cynic, as the Scriptures imply. A devil with bat
wings and horns and tail did not inveigle Jesus into the
wilderness for the test. The record says Jesus was led up
by the Spirit, by an inner compulsion."

"Do you believe there were beasts in that wilderness?"
asked an older man.

"Of course I do," said Robert, "but I don't think the
beasts were all bears and jackals."

"What do you mean?"

"I mean there are beasts which are apt to be sleeping warm in the blood of all mankind and which war with the angels of our better nature."

"Could you give examples?" asked the man.

"A ruthless industrialist may swoop down on his competitor the way the blue hawk swoops down on a field mouse. Or the she-grizzly scratching her mark on a tree — she's a little like the socialite trying to make her mark on the social register. Oh, I'll admit there's one difference: the socialite tints her claws!"

Another man raised his hand. "Bishop, I've never been able to get steamed up about theology," he said. "How do you feel about it?"

Robert said that one of the greatest theologians in Scotland once said that the Savior of the world came also for the "untheologically minded."

"There has to be 'A Constitution and Canons,'" Robert continued, "but we know very well that Canon Ninety-nine, Section Eight, Subsection Thirteen, sometimes makes it impossible for the Body of Christ to move even an eyelash! We have to have what we call a doctrine, just as He had a doctrine. But when there was too much of doctrine or it got in the way or confused and hindered people, what did He say? He said, 'Never mind now about the doctrine. Do my will, and you shall know doctrine.'"

As Robert was leaving the meeting, a wild-eyed high-school boy who had heckled him earlier during breakfast came up to him. "Bishop," he said, "I still can't go along with you. I'm still convinced — absolutely convinced — that this Jesus of yours was just a myth."

Robert smiled. "Then why can't you let Him alone?"

The boy looked surprised.

"You can't let Him alone," said Robert. "He is like the eyes of a portrait I once saw. Hang that portrait anywhere you will, and the eyes will follow you, wherever you move."

CHAPTER XXIII

Lloyd Douglas and a Trip to New York

As TIME WENT ON, Kathleen and Dee broke the news that a second grandchild was on the way. When the day came for Kathleen to enter St. Luke's Hospital, Robert announced plaintively, "But Amy, I have to go to Sedalia!"

"How like a man!" said Amy, laughing. "And just what would you have done to help, if you had been here?"

At 4:30 that afternoon, Robert called the hospital.

"It won't be long now, Bishop," said an official on the other end of the line.

Robert boarded the train and was en route to Sedalia when Kathleen's little boy was born.

In the delivery room, the doctor threw the baby up into the air to "start things going."

"And here's our little bishop!" said the doctor.

When Robert arrived at Sedalia, one of the local vestrymen rushed up with the news. "Your son-in-law just called. It's a boy! Robert Nelson Spencer DeYong!"

"How is she? How is Kathleen?"

"Fine, she's just fine and looking forward to introducing you two."

Robert that evening preached at a Confirmation service. In his sermon, he spoke of the way Christ commended His mother to the care of Saint John. "It has implications far greater than the loving act of a son toward the mother who bore him. Because of that tender act on Calvary a new mercy, a new consideration was born in the world."

After the service he went to the sacristy to remove his vestments.

"That gold cross of yours shines so bright in the candle-light!" said a little old lady.

Robert fingered the cross and studied it for a moment. "See those dents?" he said smiling. "They were made by little Amy, my granddaughter. She cut her teeth on this cross."

"How many grandchildren do you have, Bishop?" she asked.

"Two as of this evening."

"This evening!" she exclaimed.

"Yes, I just got word when I arrived that I have a grand-son — a namesake in fact."

Robert went to the Rectory and called home. "So it's Robert and Amy, is it?" he said. "How good to hear the familiar names linked in still another generation! They told me the news the moment I got off the train."

At Christmastime Robert made repeated appeals for what he called his Society for the Prevention of Useless Giving.

"If the song which the angels heard and the star which the Wise Men followed have left our sky, let us neverthe-less be content," he told one congregation. For, he ex-plained, one could hear the peace and good will of that song in the treble voice of a child singing and perhaps even catch a gleam of the Wise Men's star in a motor's headlights bearing gifts as holy as gold, frankincense, and myrrh to the homes of Christ's poor.

What is the real miracle of Christmas? Bishop Spencer said, "It is that the Christ Child reaches his tiny hand across the gulf of twenty centuries and jams the traffic of a great city weeks before his birthday."

Robert's own "Prayer for Christmas" began to be printed widely in periodicals and even appeared on Christmas cards:

Blessed art Thou, O Christmas Christ, that Thy cradle was so low that shepherds, poorest and simplest of all earthly folk, could yet kneel beside it, and look level-eyed into the face of God. Blessed art Thou, that Thy cradle was so high that the Magi, lords of learning and wealth, could yet come to it by a Star's pathway, to hazard their wisdom's store into Thy Baby hands. Blessed art Thou that, having grown to manhood, and being a carpenter, Thou didst fashion a Christmas Altar, like unto Thy cradle, so that all simplicity and all wisdom, all poverty and all wealth, all righteousness and all penitence for sin, might find sanctuary there. Be this our Christmas haste, O Christmas Christ, to seek that Altar, and, at this season of Thy Birth, unafraid of the Time's complaint, may we be found kneeling still. Amen.

Robert had read with interest two early works by a Protestant clergyman named Lloyd C. Douglas. Although both books, *Those Disturbing Miracles* and *These Sayings of Mine*, enjoyed only moderate success with the general public, they became hotly debated works in clerical circles, where they were criticized as "heretical" and "unorthodox."

From purely religious books Mr. Douglas turned to novels built on religious themes. For, as he later told Robert when they became friends, he knew that to reach the public an author has to go where they are and not expect the public to come to him. Where the average reader would not pick up a religious book, he said, he or she *would* read a love story.

Mr. Douglas told Robert he had decided to take the dynamite of Christian Theology and hide it right in the middle of a romantic story where it would explode "right in the face of some teenager out in Hollywood." He said he decided to take a Christian theme like "He who would save his life must lose it" and put it in the middle of a novel where it would hit his young reader between the eyes just when she thought she was reading about a "marriage between December and May."

Were such novels "preachy"? Many critics thought so, but the public began putting the Lloyd Douglas books high on best-seller lists — books like *Magnificent Obsession*, *Precious Jeopardy*, and recently a new novel called *Green Light* which had, as a central figure, crippled Dean Harcourt of a Midwestern cathedral, a man who spoke strangely like Robert himself.

Lloyd Douglas visited Kansas City to speak to the Women's Club. Robert and he had often corresponded, and Mr. Douglas said he had often read articles and addresses which the Bishop had written.

"You know," Mr. Douglas said, "I suspect I had you in mind when I created the character of Dean Harcourt in *Green Light*."

"No wonder I agreed with so many things the Dean said!" said Robert. "I *was* a bit suspicious. The setting was a Trinity Cathedral in a Midwestern city, a church which sounded very much like Grace and Holy Trinity, my old parish. Did you know we have made it a Cathedral now?"

The two men then talked at length and found out how much in agreement they were, despite some differences in theology.

In 1937 the Presiding Bishop's Book for Lent appeared, which included six of Robert's sermons and prayers. Typical of the poetic imagery in his style was the prayer in the book with which he concluded a talk on salvation:

Thou Merciful God, how shall we escape Thee, pursuing Hound of Heaven! In the far country of our disobedience Thy footfall halts by us; we hear a knock, and it is Thy nail-pierced hand. Again, our boat flounders in the seas of selfishness, and the Wounded Pilot takes command. We bolt and bar doors and windows. Then comest Thou and standest in the midst. If we perish, it will be in spite of Thee. It is not Thy will that even a little one shall perish. Save us, O God.

As his reputation grew, more and more preaching assignments took him to far parts of the country — St. Paul's Church, Baltimore; the Harris Theater in Chicago; a preaching mission in Santa Rosa, California; Christ Church, Houston; and many of the great churches of New York City.

The first time he preached in the huge Cathedral of St. John the Divine, Bishop Manning asked him, "How did you like it?"

"Bishop," said Robert, "it's like hollerin' down a rain barrel!"

Robert said he looked forward to his visits to New York to preach at noonday services during Lent, "that brief period when Episcopalians are said to believe in Sin." For several years, the Reverend G. Paull T. Sargent, Rector of St. Bartholomew's Church, invited him to preach a week-long series of sermons at noon.

"St. Bart's" proved quite a change of pace from the rural churches Bishop Spencer visited each week. Ushers on

Sunday mornings, dressed in cutaways and striped trousers, were a far cry from Neosho, a tiny mission which
could have fit in the choir room of St. Bartholomew's with
room to spare.

"Amy," Robert wrote, "it's all so different. You should
see the ushers at St. Bart's when they walk up toward the
sanctuary with the offering and stand in a sort of V-formation. I just know if God should ever make Himself manifest during the singing of *Old Hundredth,* the Senior Warden would probably hold up his hand and say, 'I'm awfully
sorry, but You'll just have to wait. You see, we're in our
V-formation now.'"

Another time he wrote, "But there's an intimate quality
about that great church, thanks to Paull Sargent. Tuesday
afternoon as we were walking through the empty nave,
Paull saw a pathetic little old lady. He stopped and said
to her, 'Do you mind praying for me? I need your help.'
Why, Amy, I could just feel that little lady's soul stretch
— just thinking she could do something for him."

On one of his trips East, Dr. Sargent took Robert to
hear Presbyterian Henry Sloan Coffin of New York's Union
Theological Seminary speak on the much-debated question
of union of the Presbyterian and Episcopal Churches.
Vigorous *pro* and *con* articles had appeared in Church and
secular periodicals. Feeling ran high on both sides. One
of the stumbling blocks to the idea of union was the Episcopal Church's insistence on maintaining its Apostolic Suc-
cession. Episcopalians were adamant that all clergy should
be ordained by an Episcopal bishop.

To try to arrive at an acceptable solution, a group of
liberal churchmen in both Churches came up with the

idea of dual ordination: "Why don't we work it so that Episcopalians ordain Presbyterians and Presbyterians ordain Episcopalians in reciprocal ordinations?"

Dr. Coffin spoke about the proposal at some length. When he was finished, the Master of Ceremonies spotted Robert in the back of the room.

"I see that the Episcopal Bishop of West Missouri is here," said he. "He's sitting at that far table. Maybe he'd like to give his views on the proposal."

Robert turned pale. All eyes were on him. He stood up, fidgeting with his napkin.

"I thank you for your interest in my opinion," he said. "Frankly, I should want to give it far more thought before expressing my views. I can only say that if I, as an Episcopal bishop, were ever called upon to lay my hands on a Presbyterian minister, I devoutly hope it will not be Henry Sloan Coffin."

People gasped. Dr. Coffin looked disturbed.

"I say this," Robert continued, "because, as a lad, I once laid hands on an electric dynamo with a pair of pliers where the insulation had worn off. The back-kick was unpleasant, to say the least. I dare say whoever lays his hands on Henry Sloan Coffin is liable to get a terrific back-kick of grace — enough to send the Archbishop of Canterbury north of Westchester County!"

The audience cheered. Dr. Coffin leaped down from the speaker's table, rushed back to where Robert was standing, and clasped his hand.

"Thank you for that!" he said. "How long will you be here? Can you preach tomorrow at our seminary?"

The next morning, Robert preached in the chapel. When the service was over, Dr. Coffin, obviously moved by

Robert's talk, told a group of students, "That, gentlemen, was homiletics! That was real preaching!"

During that trip East, Robert attended a number of sessions of the Hymnal Commission which was working on the compilation of a new Episcopal hymnal. At one such session, a number of the clergy got into quite a discussion about whether or not to include a new children's hymn "I sing a song of the saints of God."

Bishop Mikell of Atlanta read the text aloud. "This one line disturbs me," he said. "It says 'One was a doctor and one was a queen, And one was a shepherdess on the green.' We know who the Doctor is. He is manifestly St. Luke. We know who the Queen is. She could well be that Queen of Hungary who was later canonized. But, gentlemen, I must confess to you: I'm hard put to it to identify the 'shepherdess on the green.'"

"I'm sure it's Eleanor Roosevelt," said Robert. The Committee howled.

When at last the new Episcopal hymnal appeared, Robert's own Confirmation hymn appeared with its closing lines:

> . . . May they continue thine, O God, for ever
> Daily increasing in the Spirit's gift,
> Until they bring the gift unto the Giver,
> Where time is ended and earth's shadows lift.

Also for the hymnal the committee had chosen Robert's original additions to the Navy hymn. To the familiar petition "For those in peril on the sea," Robert's two stanzas added appeals for God's protection for those traveling by land or air as well:

... O Christ, the lord of hill and plain,
O'er which our traffic runs amain
By mountain pass or valley low;
Wherever, Lord, thy brethren go,
    Protect them by thy guiding hand
    From every peril on the land.

O Spirit, whom the Father sent
To spread abroad the firmament:
O Wind of heaven, by thy might
Save all who dare the eagle's flight,
    And keep them by thy watchful care
    From every peril in the air ...

At St. Bartholomew's Robert preached one day on prayer, and spoke particularly of the Lord's Prayer.

"What does that prayer say?" he said to the noonday congregation. "It says that Fatherhood — not 'Fatherland' — is over all. It is God's Name hallowed among His children. It is His Kingdom coming, though it may seem to come so slowly. It is His will to be done here on earth as it is in heaven, for it is one will. It is bread for today, bread eaten in unselfishness, and in trust that tomorrow's bread will not fail us. It is that we may be forgiven our sins, having first made that forgiveness possible by forgiving others. It is that we may not be led into temptation so deep and so grievous that we may not be delivered from the evil. That is the silence of eternity interpreted by that simple but profound prayer. And that is why Christians, almost universally, have used that prayer, 'by intention,' we say, when words have not come readily to their own lips."

After the service, a woman came up to Robert who had been for years a communicant of Grace and Holy Trinity

before moving to New York. He could see that she was
angry.

"I want to ask you a question," she said when they were
alone.

She told Robert about a man she knew who had stolen
money from his father's business but had never gone to
jail because he managed to borrow enough to pay back
the firm before his father's partners brought suit against
him.

"I was in the Cathedral in Dallas last fall," she continued, "and Bishop, I saw that man at the Communion.
I want you to explain that to me, if you can."

Robert asked, "What was done at that Communion
service?"

"I don't understand what you mean," said the woman.
"The man was at the altar."

Robert said, "I don't mean what this man was doing.
You told me that. But what was the priest doing? Was
he holding up a cup full of dark wine, and was he saying:
'This is my Blood of the New Testament, which is shed
for you, and for many, for the remission of sins'?"

"Yes, he said that, of course," said the woman, obviously puzzled by the question.

"Then," said Robert, "that answers your question. That's
why the man was there. Have you another question?"

"Well, I cannot forgive him," she said defiantly.

"You don't have to forgive him, not on his account; but
you had better forgive him on your own, as you value your
soul."

The woman said she did not understand what Robert
meant.

"I can believe that you don't understand," Robert went

on, "or you'd never have made the statement you just
made. Do you know the Lord's Prayer which I preached
about a few minutes ago?"

"Of course I know the Lord's Prayer."

"Do you really know it?" Robert asked. "Do you know
the very pith of that prayer? It is on the sole condition
that we forgive others that we are to be forgiven ourselves.
Our Lord gave us that prayer, and that particular petition
He bought and paid for with His most precious Blood!"

All afternoon Robert could not get that woman with her
angry face out of his mind. That evening he had to
preach in another church.

Dear God, could there be another like her, another of
the millions who only profess to call themselves Christians? he thought.

During the service he kept searching the faces of those
people in the pews. He wondered how many were there
like that, who lived "as if Jesus had never lived, as if He
had never died"? Did they let that petition in the Lord's
Prayer trip off their lips and not even know in what deeps
they were?

That evening Robert preached on the Fatherhood of
God.

"The Creed does not say: 'I believe in the Almighty,' "
he began. "It says, 'I believe in God the Father Almighty.'
It is no accident that the Creed stations God's fatherhood
as a sentry before we reach His Almightiness. And the
countersign is 'Love.' "

CHAPTER XXIV

"Boss" Pendergast and a Night Ride

IT WAS SAID that Political Boss Tom Pendergast had Kansas City by the throat. He was in the cement business, the liquor business, the racing business, and just about every other business in the city.

One man told Robert, "If we put up a building without that man's cement, the city inspectors are sure to come around and condemn the place! Why, Bishop, it's frightening, what's going on in this city."

Federal Judge Albert L. Reeves called for an investigation of election practices, because, he said, "we can't surrender the ballot to thugs, gangsters, and plug-uglies." Some state leaders tried to enact legislation that would call a halt to so-called "ghost voters" — of which there were an estimated forty thousand in one primary. As Arthur Krock reported in the *New York Times* in 1937, "For years the *Star* and groups of indignant citizens have battered away at the boss and the machine, only to find them growing stronger in the city and taking control of the politics of the State. From maker of Mayors, Sheriffs, and Councilmen, Mr. Pendergast had become the Warwick of Governors and Senators."

Citizens did get "up in arms," but Tom Pendergast continued to run Kansas City and sit by the hour in his easy chair, eating ice cream by the quart.

"Now look at me," he said. "I'm not bragging when I say I run the show in Kansas City. I am boss. If I were a Republican, they would call me a 'leader,' but 'boss' is good enough for me." Said the *New York Times:* "His self-defined rule in politics is: 'By God, we feed 'em and we vote 'em.'"

Several times callers came to Robert's study with petitions from Boss Pendergast. Sometimes they were people he knew. Often they were total strangers, sent to get Robert to endorse this or that document.

"Mr. Pendergast said if we could just get your endorsement on this paper . . ." the caller inevitably declared.

One day a man named C. J. Ransom came to the study. He had a letter from Pendergast.

"If you will sign your name to this letter," said Mr. Ransom, "Mr. Pendergast said that it will land me a job with any one of these four companies. But he insisted, Bishop, that I get your signature on this letter as well as his own."

Robert's face reddened. "Who does this man think he is!" he fumed. "What right has this man to dictate whom these firms should hire? Is he a stockholder? Where did he get his power? Mr. Ransom, this makes me livid. It's wicked. It's all wrong."

Robert was pacing back and forth across the room.

"Don't you see what he's up to, Mr. Ransom?" said he.

"No, I'm afraid I don't," said the man.

"Pendergast wants me to be beholden to him for this favor. Oh, he's tried this before, Mr. Ransom, many times. He wants to tell people, 'See, Bishop Spencer's on my side. See, he's a friend of mine. I can show you right here. Look at this letter he signed.'"

Robert turned to Mr. Ransom. "No," he said, "I'll sign nothing of the kind. I'll be happy to help arrange a job interview for you at one of these companies. I'll be glad to do it, but it will be my own letter. It'll be my own doing, because I know you have ability and not because you ever came to me at that man's urging."

"Do you know Mr. Pendergast?" asked Mr. Ransom.

"I've met him only once," said Robert.

"When was that?"

Robert smiled. "At a gangster's funeral," he explained. "I met him at a gangster's funeral where the soloist sang — of all things! — 'When You Come to the End of a Perfect Day.'"

Mr. Ransom laughed. He thanked Robert, apologized for coming to him as he did, and walked to the door.

"May I help set up an interview for you?" Robert asked.

"No, thank you, Bishop," said Mr. Ransom. "I'd like to see if I couldn't do this on my own."

A few weeks later, as more and more callers made their way from Pendergast to the Bishop's study, Robert decided to take the issue into the pulpit.

"It's dangerous, Robert," Amy warned. "There are sure to be repercussions."

"I've got to talk about this man," said Robert. "This has gone too far. I must speak up."

"But Robert, that's dangerous," said Amy. "Besides you've always said you didn't think a preacher should waste his time rehashing the political debates his people have to wade in up to the chins in their papers every day of the week."

"This is different, Amy. It's gone too far," said Robert.

"Besides, look what Sam Mayerberg is doing. He isn't standing on the side lines!"

On Sunday, July 5, Robert declared: "There was a lot of noise in this city last night. You were whooping it up about the freedom of our country and its independence from an old king by the name of George the Third, a king who was beaten by a George the First who was 'first in war, first in peace, and first in the hearts of his countrymen.' But he died over a hundred years ago, and you are still making a lot of noise about it. Well, you've got a tyrant right here that can give George the Third hearts and spades."

Members of the congregation looked at one another. Many of them shifted nervously in their seats.

"Look at the Declaration of Independence," Robert continued in a loud voice. "What does it say? He sent among us 'the merciless Indian savages, whose known rule of warfare is an undistinguished destruction of all ages, sexes, and conditions.' Very well. Now let us look at your Declaration today, in Nineteen Hundred and Now. What will it say? 'He has sent among us automobiles full of hoodlums and gangsters with sawed-off shotguns to intimidate us at the polls and to keep us from our rights of franchise as free American citizens.' Why don't you make some noise about *him?* Why don't you burn a lot of powder about *him?* . . ."

Robert then proceeded to go straight down the Declaration of Independence, phrase by phrase, pointing out the deadly parallel between the statements about George the Third and what might be said about the tyrant of Kansas City.

The minute the service was over, a reporter rushed

up to Robert. "Could you let me have your manuscript?" he asked. "I couldn't take notes fast enough."

An hour later the phone rang. It was the editor of the *Star*.

"Bishop Spencer," said the man, "that sermon you preached this morning was dynamite. The reporter who covered it showed me the manuscript you gave him. Bishop, we want very much to print it, but we have such high regard for you, we wanted to check with you first. You're sure to have reprisals."

"I'm not afraid," said Robert. "I'd like to have you print it. You may even put it on the front page if you like."

The account did appear. A number of threatening letters followed.

As one anonymous person put it, "Bishop, if I had been present when you preached that sermon attacking Mr. Pendergast, *you would never have left that church alive!*"

More than once at services Robert read the familiar old collect from the prayer book:

Grant us grace fearlessly to contend against evil, and to make no peace with oppression; and, that we may reverently use our freedom, help us to employ it in the maintenance of justice among men and nations . . .

Those were the words Robert used. His own part in Sam Mayerberg's crusade against the Pendergast regime, it was said, showed that he meant every one of them.

Leaders in many areas of Kansas City played their own important roles in the long, hard fight to unseat Boss Pendergast. Among religious leaders Robert's friend Sam perhaps waged the fiercest fight. Finally, on May 22, 1939, when Mr. Pendergast pleaded guilty to tax-evasion charges and was sentenced to a Federal penitentiary, the Boss's regime came to an end at last.

In 1939 Robert was asked to serve as acting Bishop of Salina, Kansas, in addition to his responsibilities in West Missouri. For three years he was to serve the people of Kansas and bear the nickname of "Bishop of the Dust Bowl."

The Kansas churchmen were most grateful to Robert for his willingness to help them while they were without a bishop of their own. They made every effort to make Robert's added work as easy as they could. On many occasions the laymen refused to let him drive himself — as he did in his own diocese — and provided him with a driver.

"This is an indulgence. I can just as well drive myself," Robert said.

"Hush!" said a forceful old lady. "We insist on it."

"But in Missouri, I always —"

"You're in Kansas now," said the lady with a tone of unconcealed pride.

One evening, Robert had to make a hurried trip to a church some distance away in Kansas, and Ridge Carson, a sandy-haired man in his early twenties, stopped by to pick him up.

"It will be quite a long haul for you, I'm afraid," said the young man.

"You are kind to take me on such short notice," said Robert.

As they drove along in the night, Ridge Carson said suddenly, "Bishop, may I talk to you about my life and about my soul?"

"Talk on," said Robert.

As he listened, the boy poured out the story of his life and the many wrongs he had done, not worse or less than the average youth. He did not excuse himself or blame his companions.

When they arrived at their destination, Ridge turned to Robert. "I hope you will not think this odd," he said, "but you know, as we were riding along in this car, it almost seemed to me that Jesus was with us."

"And so He was," said Robert softly. "He is where there are two or three. I dare say He was with us as surely as He was with those disciples on the lake in the night, and He would have been asleep on the pillow, if we had not called on Him to help us."

"I know you must be right," said Ridge.

"I have great hopes for you," said Robert. "You're honest, and there's life and feeling in your soul. The old adage, 'While there is life, there is hope,' is as true for the soul as it is for the physical body."

"I suppose that's true," said Ridge thoughtfully.

"Of course, it's true," Robert continued. "Why do you suppose men cross a continent to Johns Hopkins or Battle Creek to get a little feeling into a dead wrist?"

"Will you remember me in your prayers, Bishop?" asked the young man.

"Of course I will," said Robert. "Your life is still before you. Think of the thrilling opportunities you have to make a mark in the world."

"What do you mean?" asked the young man.

"Sure, you've made mistakes," Robert continued, "but your job is to pick yourself up and keep going."

Robert reminded the boy that everyone has more influence in the world than he realizes, that even the seemingly unimportant things he might do or say have a lasting effect on lives about him.

"You know, God works in the world, even when we don't do our part," Robert said finally. "The old saying that God can work *only* through our hands is all wrong. As Christians, of course, we try to fulfill God's highest hopes for our individual lives. We try to do so, not because we think we're pretty grand. We try to do so, because we want to share in God's work in the world and because we haven't the heart to let Him down."

Ridge Carson, much moved by what the Bishop had said, looked at Robert for a moment. He said nothing, then picked up the two suitcases and led the way up the walk to the house where Robert was to spend what remained of the night.

CHAPTER XXV

Courage before Bullets

THE NIGHT BEFORE HE LEFT for a speaking tour, Robert excused himself to go work on his income tax. After he left the next morning, as she was cleaning up the study, Amy was exasperated to find on his desk only a blank tax form and beside it, instead, a poem about Zacchaeus! Across the top of the page, Robert had written:

And Zacchaeus stood, and said unto the Lord . . . the half of my goods I give to the poor; and if I have taken any thing from any man by false accusation I restore him fourfold. —ST. LUKE XIX:8.

This Zacchaeus of Holy Writ
    Was long on revenue.
He must have had a head on him,
    Though he was short to view.

Jesus passed through his town one day;
    The better Whom to see,
This four-foot-five of Revenue
    Did shinny up a tree.

Jesus, he smiled on Zacchaeus:
    "Descend, good man, I say;
For I would have a talk with you,
    Ere comes the Judgment Day."

They talked. The gorger did disgorge,
    And what he'd done undo —
Do all the Income Taxers so?
    Just name me one or two!

Amy looked at the blank tax form still waiting to be filled out.

The man's incorrigible, she told herself.

That winter, Robert had to be on the road much of the time preaching.

During one sermon in Michigan, he pulled a pulpit loose from its moorings.

"We never bother to fasten our pulpit down," someone explained. "You see, our Dean speaks without notes."

"So does our parrot!" Robert said, and he took off for Chicago.

Three days later, Robert was scheduled to give the first of a series of noonday Lenten sermons at one of the downtown theaters. At noon the phone rang in his hotel room.

"Why aren't you here, Bishop?" asked a frantic voice. "It's 12:15! You should be here at the theater preaching. You're late. You're on the air!"

"I'm what?"

"On the air!"

"How am I doing?" Robert asked. Within ten minutes he had reached the theater and breathlessly begun his sermon.

That afternoon, the phone rang. A half-hysterical woman was on the other end of the line.

"Bishop, Bishop," she sobbed. "Can I come see you? I heard you this noon. I've got to see you. Bishop, it's a matter of life and death. My husband's in danger. You are the one person who can help — I know you can."

"Where are you now?" Robert asked.

"At the police station out near Cicero," said the woman.

"The chief here says he doesn't know if my husband will get out of this alive or not."

"Stay where you are," the Bishop said. "I'll grab a taxi and be right out."

It took him fully an hour and a half to find the right police station. When he arrived, the man at the door ushered him at once down the hall to a dingy little conference room where three police officers were trying to comfort the woman — Maria Tedesco, a handsome, dark-haired girl in her late twenties. The moment she saw Robert, Maria leaped up.

"Thank God!" she shrieked, running toward him.

Slowly, in the hour which followed, Maria and the police explained the whole story in detail to Robert. Apparently, the husband, Joe Tedesco, who had grown up in the slums of Chicago, had become mixed up with the notorious Tully gang. For three years he was glorified messenger boy for the "inner circle," until he was himself caught by the police during a "bank job," convicted, and sentenced to five years in jail. When finally he was released from prison, he was determined to "go straight" and took a job at the garage owned by Maria's father. In the course of the summer he met Maria, fell in love with her, and asked her to marry him. He told Maria again the whole story of his years with the Tully gang and how he had spent the five years in jail. "But it makes no difference," said Maria. "You've gone straight." That September they were married.

In January a few members of the old Tully gang learned of Joe's whereabouts and offered him money if he would get out of town. Maria had protested.

"But with Papa you have work," she said. "Somewhere else, without Papa, you might not find it so easy to get work."

Joe had decided to stay on. The Tully men began writing threatening letters. Finally, that Monday morning, they had beaten Joe up and taken him to an old brownstone house four blocks from the police station where they were holding him captive.

"They won't give him up, and I'm afraid they'll kill him," said the sergeant.

"Can't you do anything?" asked Robert.

"We've tried just about everything."

"Have you talked to the men?"

"It doesn't do any good, Bishop. We can't get near the place," said the sergeant. "We tried tear gas. It didn't do any good. They've got a fresh air vent in there we can't seem to locate."

"Could you surround the place?" asked Robert.

"It is surrounded now," said the police sergeant. "Frankly, I'm afraid to let my men move in on the place. I know these people. I'm afraid they'll kill Joe."

"What do you think we can do?" asked Robert.

The three policemen looked at Robert.

"Maria here thinks you are our one hope," said the sergeant.

"Me! What can I do?" asked Robert.

"You can enter that house unarmed. You're a clergyman. Sure, it's a chance. You'll be in danger, but I'll have you covered from the outside."

"What good would *that* do me, inside the place?" asked Robert.

"Not much, I'm afraid."

Maria looked at Robert. "I heard you today. I heard what you said in that theater."

Robert said, "Do you honestly think if I go in there, I'll ever get out alive?"

"Yes, I do," said Maria. "I know about these men. Call it superstition. Call it fear. Call it whatever you want. I know they would not dare hurt you. You're a priest."

Robert sat, thoughtfully staring at the little window opposite him.

Maria came over to him and took the chair beside him. "Don't you see, Bishop? If the police try to go in there, Joe will never get out alive. If I go in there, they'll never listen. They'll kill both of us. Bishop, you can save Joe's life."

At 5:35 that afternoon, a cordon of police covered the front steps of the house as Robert nervously crossed the street, went up the stairs, and entered the darkened house.

"Who's there?" cried a deep voice from upstairs.

Robert said nothing but slowly made his way up the dark stairs to the one room where he could see light shining. He entered the room slowly. The surprised gangsters gasped.

"God, a priest!" said one man by the door.

Robert took no notice of the armed men but walked directly to Joe Tedesco, who was tied to a straight-backed chair which stood against the wall.

The look on Joe's face showed as much surprise as the faces of the Tully men.

Robert spoke reassuringly to Joe. "Maria is safe. I have just seen her."

Robert said nothing to the gangsters directly, but spoke only to Joe, making sure the others clearly overheard him.

He told Joe that the Tully men were trapped in the house. If they killed him, the police would capture them in a matter of minutes. Dead or alive, they would have another murder to answer for.

"What have these men to gain in losing their lives because they take yours, Joe?" Robert went on. "If they allow you to leave the house alive, the police would certainly be more lenient. It's their only chance."

Robert stood there a minute. His heart had been pounding. Now a strange calm came over him.

"I don't believe God intended you to be killed in this way," Robert said slowly and deliberately. "I am going to untie you. You are going to follow me out of the house. These men will let you go alive. They know now that it is their only chance."

Robert untied the captive, still not looking toward the armed men across the room.

"Let 'em go!" said a voice. "I won't have the blood of a priest on my conscience."

With Joe directly behind him, Robert walked to the door, down the stairs and out into the street. In a moment they entered the building across the street where Maria and the sergeant were waiting.

"Joe! Joe!" Maria shrieked, throwing her arms around her husband.

"Baby!" said Joe, hugging his sobbing wife tightly.

"What ever did you do, Bishop?" asked the sergeant. "What ever did you say to talk them out of —"

Robert looked at Joe and Maria who stood watching him.

"You should have heard him, Sarge!" said Joe.

"How did you know what to say?" asked the sergeant.

Robert smiled. "Prayer tells you what to say. In a sense, I let Someone else do the talking — a lesson I learned a long time ago."

CHAPTER XXVI

Pastor Pastorum

DESPITE HIS MANY EARLY YEARS of poor health, Robert's ministry was marked by few occasions when illness kept him from his duties. It was like him, Amy said, to rise from a sickbed to make a scheduled speech, like the time he crossed half a continent with a temperature of a hundred and three to address a mass meeting.

Robert's wild shock of hair now began to turn gray and the fast pace he set for himself had given his face a haggard look.

"I suppose I'm a pompous ass," he confessed, "to think the universe would stop if I missed a Ladies' Aid, but as long as I can, I plan to keep going at my present rate of speed!"

Just as when he was rector of Grace and Holy Trinity, now as Bishop of West Missouri Robert enjoyed very cordial relationships with the clergy of other churches. Not only with his friend Sam Mayerberg, but with others as well, he worked hard on charitable and cultural crusades, fraternized with them in a way that meant no one's views on faith and worship were compromised.

On interchurch panels and forums, the Bishop could not be inveigled into a religious row. This did not mean compromise, far from it; it meant that he respected other men's convictions, and that he did not propose to surrender his own, as he said, "in a Donnybrook Fair."

"Mere opinions are like thistledown blown on the winds," he told friends. "It's convictions that build cathedrals and churches and meetinghouses. When convictions clash with convictions, there's no place to meet. It's like a duel between a dog and a fish. If the duel is fought on the shore, the fish will be drowned in the air; if it's fought offshore, the dog will be drowned."

Among Robert's good friends were two Roman Catholic leaders, Monsignor James Keyes and Monsignor James S. V. McKay. Father Keyes was indeed a kind of father to all children, regardless of religion, race, or color. It was he who was largely responsible for the building of a stadium and a ball park.

Once when Monsignor Keyes was thought to be dying in St. Joseph's Hospital, one of Robert's own priests, making calls there, knocked on the Monsignor's door.

"Do come in," said a doctor. "He's conscious now, but you may stay only a minute."

The young man went to the bedside. "I'm here for Bishop Spencer," he said. "He told me to tell you that eleven thousand Episcopalians are praying for your recovery."

The Monsignor turned to his doctor, smiling. "Wouldn't it beat hell if those Episcopalian prayers got me out of here!"

On a state occasion at his church, Monsignor McKay made a special point of inviting Robert to be present at the service and sit with the Monsignor's sister in a front pew.

As the silent procession of dignitaries came up the aisle,

Monsignor McKay stopped, turned to Robert, and said in a loud voice that could be heard in the street, "Good morning, Bishop Spencer, and a hearty welcome to you!"

Robert was quite startled, but no one else in the church appeared to be.

"It was an elaborate service," he told Amy later. "That chain of ritual had every link of Rome's ornate symbolism, and yet it did not lack Rome's truly superb ease."

Robert was invited on one occasion to take part in a dinner in honor of a visiting cardinal, at the Hotel Muehlebach. Before going into the banquet hall Robert and the Cardinal were swapping stories when a line of Roman Catholics approached the Cardinal to kiss his ring.

Robert stepped back, but the Cardinal spotted him.

"Come back here, Bishop," he said, "I want you to get into the huddle."

For he well knew that neither would try to steal the other team's signals.

The early 1940's proved busy years for Robert. With war came added responsibility to the armed forces' installations within the Diocese. As Head of the Board of St. Luke's Hospital, he continued to work hard to enable the institution to meet the growing needs of a growing city. Scribner's published a collection of his sermons in book form, called *The Seer's House;* and Dickinson College, which had already honored him with a Doctor of Divinity degree, conferred upon him a Doctor of Laws degree at ceremonies attended by his old classmates Dan Ray and Charlie Evans.

Despite the curtailed travel of those years, many guests found their way to the Spencer home on West 47th Street.

The Bishop of Polynesia, for instance, stopped off at Kansas City and came round to the Spencers'.

"Should we offer him a drink?" Kathleen asked her husband. "That poor old man looks bushed."

In a moment she produced a glass of sherry and handed it to the guest.

They all waited tensely for the Polynesian Bishop's reaction.

"This is indeed a Christian household!" said the old man. "Cheers!"

One autumn evening Robert, who had spoken at a town some distance from Kansas City, climbed aboard a sleeper train which was parked on a siding and went to bed.

About midnight, two vestrymen from a nearby parish came aboard, and asked the porter to show them to Robert's berth.

"Sorry to disturb you," said Mr. Warren, "but it's rather urgent, Bishop. It's about our rector."

Robert put on his dressing gown and followed the two men to the empty lounge.

"Bishop, people are talking, and talking plenty," said Mr. Randall.

"There are all sorts of rumors about the rector," said Mr. Warren. "They're dynamite. I'm afraid they'll split the parish wide open."

"Yes," said Mr. Randall, "and we wanted you to know about the situation direct instead of hearing the rumors later on, second or third hand."

Then they proceeded to tell the whole story, how people claimed the rector had taken to drink. Robert listened quietly.

"Thank you for coming to me," he said finally. "I am

grateful to you. Naturally, there's nothing I can do about this situation tonight."

"We just wanted you to know," said Mr. Warren.

"Yes, I understand," said Robert. "Of course, I shall want to check the facts myself. And remember, gentlemen, we're dealing with a man's life. In fact, we're dealing with the life of his whole family."

"We understand that," said Mr. Randall.

"I don't want to act hastily," Robert said as he rose from his seat. "This week, I'm having all of our clergy in for their annual retreat. Your rector will be there."

The two men said good night, apologized again for their intrusion, and left.

Later that week, all the clergy arrived at the Spencers' house for the annual retreat. The young rector came. As he told his wife later, he had no idea Robert had heard the rumors.

"I only knew that the Bishop seemed to be addressing a lot of his remarks directly at me," he said. "He said a lot about penitence, forgiveness, and the Christian idea of a second chance. A few days later, of course, I found out why."

For Robert left Kansas City and drove down to see the young priest. He explained that he had heard all the rumors and wanted to learn his own side of the story.

The priest admitted the rumors had been true, but said he was trying to cure himself of the habit and needed help.

"Under the circumstances I am going to have to suspend you," said Robert, "I plan to move you to Kansas City, to put you in touch with a good doctor I know can help you. I plan to let you stay there until you are back on your feet again."

At first the Spencers had the young priest stay in their house. Then Robert rented a house for the man and his family and gave them a modest allowance.

One bitterly cold day, when the local clergy met at the Cathedral to hear a paper read, Robert excused himself.

One of the other priests followed him out into the hall. "Is there something I can do for you? You don't want to miss hearing the paper," he said.

"I'd like to hear the paper read," said Robert, "but I've got an errand to do."

"You're not traipsing over to that problem child's house again, are you?" asked the priest.

"Yes," said Robert. "I'm taking him some coal."

"Honestly, Bishop, I don't understand you," said the man. "If I were you, I'd let him refrigerate a bit."

"I'd like to hear that paper read," said Robert quietly, "but I'll be honest with you: I wouldn't hear a word of it, if I were thinking that those three children had to — 'refrigerate,' as you call it."

That evening, Robert wrote an eight-page letter to a missionary bishop in the West, telling him all about the young rector, why he had suspended him, what he had done. In his letter he expressed the hope that some new work might be found for him.

Back came the reply. "I'm a good deal older bishop than you are," the missionary bishop wrote, "but you have written me the most apostolic letter I have ever received from a bishop. I wouldn't make a place for even my brother in this district, but I will find a place for your man. Send him on."

At church the next Sunday, Robert preached on forgiveness and told the story about how Saint Jerome one

Christmas night had said he wished to give a present to the Infant Jesus.

"First he offered the Infant Jesus his monumental works on the Holy Scriptures," said Robert. "Then he offered his labors for the conversion of souls. Then he offered such virtues of his as he was able to offer. But all these were not what the Infant Jesus wanted. 'Jerome,' He said, 'it is thy *sins* I wished for. Give them to me that I may pardon them.'"

CHAPTER XXVII

Heart Attack

ONE COLD AFTERNOON in 1948 Amy saw Robert put on his coat and go out for some air.

"I'm worried about your father," she said to Kathleen. She had gone to the window and was watching him go down the street. "He's all worn out. I think he looks haggard."

"He's just had flu, Mother, after all."

"I know, but he won't let up," said Amy. "He's been working morning, noon, and night on those letters for the hospital, and he insists on doing them all himself."

"What's the rush?"

"He says people who gave money for the new wing are wondering why we still haven't started building."

Friends, too, had said that they noticed a change — that Robert was looking pale these days. His wild gray hair seemed as thick as ever, but the nervous hand which brushed it back looked older.

"But you must remember," Dee said, "he's not a young man. After all, he's seventy-one."

Amy watched Robert head toward the park, just two blocks away.

When he reached the park, a sudden sharp pain hit him in the chest. He doubled up, then staggered toward a tree to steady himself. Pain shot through his arm, and he felt sick at his stomach.

Instead of lying down on the grass until help came, Robert made his way to the sidewalk and headed back up the two blocks toward home. By the time he climbed the steps, went back in the house, and finally pulled himself up to his room, it was all he could do to call out "Amy! Amy!" and flop down on the bed.

"Get the doctor!" Amy called to Kathleen a few moments later. "It's your father."

Within minutes Dr. Hashinger arrived at the house, hurried upstairs, and examined Robert. He gave him a shot of morphine.

"I'm afraid it's a coronary," said he, going out into the hall.

"How serious do you think it is?" asked Amy.

"We can't tell yet."

"What are you going to do — take him to the hospital?" she asked.

"No," said Dr. Hashinger. "I don't want him jolted in an ambulance. I'll get oxygen over here to you just as soon as I can."

Robert called out weakly for Amy. She went back to his room.

"I may not get well," he said.

"Please, don't even try to talk," she said.

"But I want things settled," he said with a thick tongue. "I can't be buried at Mount Washington. I must be buried at St. Luke's burial ground like the other bishops."

"Buried?" said Dr. Hashinger. "We're not going to let you die."

Robert mumbled something and began to doze off.

Three hours later, he had another attack.

"I'm going to call the hospital this time," said Dr. Hashinger, after examining his patient.

In less than an hour, Robert, gravely ill and under heavy sedation, had been moved to the hospital.

With Robert's admission to St. Luke's, the news was out, and the telephone at the Spencers' began to ring. The calls continued all day — most of them from friends, but many from strangers whom Robert had helped in one way or another.

At the hospital, telegrams, flowers, messages of all sorts began pouring in — among them roses from Rabbi Mayerberg and the Temple B'Nai Jehudah, and an enormous arrangement from Robert's friend Monsignor McKay.

But the medical reports, carried each day in the *Star*, gave wellwishers little encouragement. Several friends, despairing of Robert's chances of pulling through, stopped by to pay their last respects. In the anteroom sat Rabbi Mayerberg, several Episcopal clergymen, a representative from Roman Catholic Bishop O'Hara, and an agnostic whom Robert had befriended.

The nurse came out to the waiting room and told the agnostic gentleman that Robert wanted to see him first.

"But Bishop," said the man, as he entered his room, "do you know who's out there? A representative from Bishop O'Hara, Rabbi Mayerberg, and a whole lot of distinguished clergymen. Why on earth did you call me in first?"

"Because I rather expect to see the others again," said Robert, smiling.

A little while later, Rabbi Mayerberg did slip in but, respecting the warning on the door, only for a minute, to give Robert his blessing, and that afternoon Father Byrnes from the Roman Catholic Cathedral also looked in on Robert.

A day or two later, the doctor noted a marked improvement in Robert's condition, and another visitor was admitted: Lieutenant General J. C. H. Lee.

Robert beamed. "So this — after forty-five years — is Cliff Lee," said he. "How good of you to remember me!"

"Did you think I would forget my Junction City rector?" Cliff asked.

Time magazine had carried Cliff's picture on the cover in 1944 when, as head of Eisenhower's Services of Supply of the European Theater of Operations, he did a near-miraculous job of keeping "supplies eternally on the go."

"Remember the time back in Junction City when you were a choir boy and turned all the lights out?"

"No, I don't," said Cliff, "but I well remember drawing a picture of you in a hymnbook and writing under it R.N.S. PREACHING TO BEAT HELL!"

Cliff drew up a chair beside Robert's bed.

"How is Mrs. Spencer?" he asked.

"We're a little worried about her," said Robert. "She seems to be having trouble with arthritis. She doesn't say much about it, but I know she's uncomfortable. I can tell by looking at her swollen hands."

Cliff explained to the Bishop that he was retiring from the army.

"What do you plan to do now?" Robert asked.

"I'm going to devote myself full time to laymen's work in the Brotherhood of St. Andrew."

"I'm glad to hear it, Cliff," said Robert. He looked at the sometime choirboy, now a three-star general. "You have the baptismal formula right," he went on. "Remember how you promised to continue Christ's faithful soldier and servant?"

"That I do, sir."

"Well, you've been a great soldier," Robert said. "Now you will be a great servant in the Brotherhood" — and he gave Cliff his blessing.

During the next few days two patients died down the hall.

"You wonder why others go and not oneself," Robert said ruefully to Amy. "I had been praying for them."

"You know the Bible verse better than I," said Amy. "How does it go? 'Two . . . shall be grinding at the mill; one shall be taken, and the other left.'"

"Do you suppose it's because the one in the field still has work to do?" Robert said thoughtfully. They were silent together. A few minutes later he added, "Well, Amy, our Lord did not answer that question, and maybe George Eliot meant we shouldn't ask when she said, somewhere, that if we could hear the grass grow or the squirrel's heartbeat, we should die of the roar that lies on the other side of silence."

When Amy left him that day, she came back only a few minutes later, all smiles. "I have news for you," she announced. "You're going home next week — Ed Hashinger just told me."

CHAPTER XXVIII

Nunc Dimittis

ON HIS NEXT BIRTHDAY, February 18, 1949, when Robert turned seventy-two, he formally announced his plan to retire following the next General Convention to be held in the fall. At the same time, he gave official consent to the election of a bishop coadjutor to be elected at the Annual Diocesan Convention to be held that next May.

For some time laymen and clergy alike had expected such an announcement. It came as no surprise. When the news broke officially, it only further stimulated the speculation as to who the next bishop would be.

"Traditionally, the Episcopal Church has never been as strong in the Missouri–Kansas–Oklahoma area as in the East and Far West," wrote one newspaper columnist. "Bishops in these areas have still much trail-blazing to do. Consequently, the choice of an effective leader is especially important."

When the time came for the convention in St. Joseph, Robert said to Amy, "I'm terribly disturbed at all the backbiting that's going on."

"What do you mean?" asked Amy.

"Oh, I've tried to keep aloof from the discussions about my successor," he said, "but I couldn't help getting wind of a lot of the vicious talk that's going on about some of the men whose names may come up for nomination."

At the opening session, Robert gave formal consent to the election. Following considerable discussion from the floor, balloting began. At first, a good many "favorite sons" were given token votes. Then the voting narrowed down to two candidates. The convention became deadlocked.

"I'm sick over the whole thing," Robert told Amy after supper. "The wrangling, the bitter whispering that's going on — it makes me feel as if my own leadership has been a failure."

"Don't be silly."

"No, I mean it," said Robert. "I feel I must not have given the proper spirit to this diocese. Everyone's so bitter. The rumormongers have left me weak with disgust. Oh, Amy dear, it breaks my heart to see the way people are carrying on. Why should I have to leave my episcopate on such a sour note?"

Robert spent a sleepless night. Early the next morning, he celebrated the Holy Communion at Christ Church. After breakfast, the speeches began again as the convention was noisily resumed.

Then, all of a sudden, a hush fell over the hall. Robert, looking very worn, had stood up and raised his hand for silence.

"It is my manifest duty," he said huskily, "in view of the fact of the spirit of this convention, its unhappy hours, that I withdraw my consent to this election. I do not believe the Holy Spirit could come within ten blocks of this meeting!"

People looked at each other.

"What's the old man up to?" whispered one heavy-set delegate.

"I withdraw consent to this election," the Bishop continued solemnly, "because, if any election ensued at this time, any self-respecting man would not want to come there as bishop coadjutor, whether he were chosen from inside or outside the diocese."

No one stirred. Robert's action had stunned the delegates.

"In mid-September of this year, when all the bishops are in place to receive my resignation," he continued, "I will be legally dead to you. I believe it would be manifestly better to have an election at that time. I cannot in all conscience fail to withdraw my consent. This withdrawal *ipso facto* concludes an election at this time."

The *Kansas City Star* reported: "There was a hush as some two hundred delegates, lay, clerical, and alternates, realized that there could be no election of a bishop at this time . . . the whole group sat down at the conclusion of Bishop Spencer's edict. There was no public objection, and no statement was forthcoming privately from individuals. Protest was indicated, however, when delegates walked out singly and in two's and three's and half-dozens. Only about a third of the group remained to carry out the concluding business. . . ."

For some days local papers continued to carry articles referring to Robert's action. Church periodicals were full of it, and letters of protest began arriving in the mail, until Amy at least became weary of the whole business.

But many understanding letters arrived in the mail, too. From a number of church leaders, fellow bishops, theological seminary teachers came appreciative messages: "Our hats are off to you!" "How wonderful that there are still some men with the courage of their convictions who

will choose the harder right instead of the easier wrong!"
"You acted with rare courage" — letters like these began
coming in, many of them from men he had never met.

"I know my action has won me outspoken enemies,"
said Robert. "Such decisions don't make you popular.
They only make you misunderstood."

The dispute had been hard on Robert, but it had been
equally hard on Amy. Both Kathleen and the doctor
became quite disturbed about how generally run down
Mrs. Spencer seemed to be.

The following October, Robert preached his last sermon as bishop, not in a church but in a greenhouse on
the edge of town where a new group was meeting. The
next day, he celebrated the Holy Communion, his farewell
service, at Grace and Holy Trinity Cathedral.

"This is what I most want," he said, "to be in this
Cathedral. And before this altar, so familiar to me, I want
to give thanks for the happy years, for your patience and
cooperation, and the fellowship we have shared."

As he spoke, his voice was charged with emotion. This
day marked the nineteenth anniversary of his consecration
as bishop in this same sanctuary.

"God bless you," he said somewhat huskily. "From
the bottom of my heart I thank you for coming here to be
with me in my last official service." Then, opening his
prayer book, he resumed the service with the words: "Let
us pray for the whole state of Christ's Church."

At the Kansas City Club that night, Robert and Amy
stood for almost two hours in the receiving line at a reception given in their honor and attended by some five
hundred of their friends.

Monsignor McKay spoke of Robert's endearing simplicity.

"I know of no man," said the Mayor of Kansas City, "who has gathered more of the spirit of the One he has served, the Prince of Peace, than Bishop Spencer."

At the end of the evening, Robert moved to the center of the room. The crowd became still.

"I am grateful," he said, "that you say you have found me to be a kind man, because I have always sought to be. Differences of opinion are a good thing and necessary, because no man could rightly be a consistent neutral. Those who were lowest in Dante's Inferno were the neutrals. A man should have the courage to take his stand, even though it be painful at times, because such differences need not damage the central heart or love that is in all of us."

Robert and Amy returned home.

"I was so proud of you," said Amy tenderly.

Robert sat down on the couch, took up his pipe and lighted it. Their little dachshund jumped up and licked his ear.

"You know, Amy," he said, "this dog is quite a pet. Why, do you know what she said to me this afternoon . . . ?"

"Robert, you're incorrigible," said Amy, putting her cheek to his.

CHAPTER XXIX

Good-by to Amy

FOR SEVERAL YEARS Amy's arthritis had been growing progressively worse; now her eyesight was beginning to fail. At Dee's instigation, the DeYongs and Spencers bought a new house together, so that Kathleen could keep a watchful eye on her mother, who she suspected was suffering far more than even Robert realized.

Kathleen went to Dr. Hashinger. "I'm worried about Mother," she said. "She's sleeping a great deal in the day-time now, and her mind seems terribly confused at times."

The doctor's diagnosis was that Amy was suffering from "pin-point strokes," and that little could be done for this condition. A cerebral occlusion later followed which impaired the eyesight still further.

"Mother knows she's slipping, but she's wonderfully brave about it," Kathleen told the doctor.

Amy knew she had become more and more confused in her thinking; so she made a point when guests came of sitting on the sofa beside Kathleen, and holding her daughter's hand.

"If I say anything strange, just press my hand," she said. "I'll know what that means and I'll be still."

In his devotion to Amy, Robert did not seem at first to realize what was happening. "He seems to live in another world so far as Mother is concerned," Kathleen maintained. Gradually, as Amy continued to fail, Robert kept asking Dr. Hashinger for assurance that she was not suffering unduly.

Amy's room had two doors — one leading to a bathroom, the other to the hall which led down to Kathleen and Dee's room. In the months which followed, Amy, nearly blind, suffered a few bad falls.

"Kathleen, I'm worried about the children," Amy said one day. "Here, they're just seeing me fall apart. I think you ought to put me in a nursing home. You must put me somewhere. I don't want to interfere with the young life in this house."

Kathleen would not hear of it, and Dr. Hashinger agreed with her.

"It's a wise thing," said the doctor, "to let young people find out about the aged. After all, their generation is going to be the one faced with the problem of the aged more than any generation to date. It will be a fine thing for them to learn a little about it now from a grandmother they adore, because it's going to be an increasingly serious problem in the years to come."

So Amy remained at home.

One evening, she told Kathleen, "You're not getting enough rest. I know you're not. You are forever coming in here when you hear me moving around. You're afraid I'm going to walk out the wrong door and fall downstairs. Well, why don't you lock my door?"

"I wouldn't think of it," said Kathleen. "All your life you've hated to be shut up in a small room. I'd rather move into your room than do that."

Amy straightened the pillow behind her. "I know you're worried about the way I wander around the house," she continued. "Why don't you get one of those chains we used to have on the front door of the other house? You could put one on the outside of my hall door. That way, you could leave the door ajar and I can't possibly walk out there and fall."

The next day, Dee bought the chain and Amy stayed, uncomplaining, in her room.

Three months later, Robert wrote to a friend:

After repeated breaking of small blood vessels in the grand brain she had, dear Amy has now become as a little child. She cannot leave her room, and she does not know us except at lucid intervals. But she is still happy, and always says "thank you" for the little kindnesses we can still do for her. I am grateful that she does not suffer, and I think her dreams are all happy. She was a saint, and it is paying dividends now that she is no more able to use her fine mind. Naturally, we all suffer for her. Not long ago, in one of her lucid intervals, she said to me: "All I can do is wait patiently for the end." But she knows that the end will be a better beginning that will be endless.

Kathleen now had to feed her every mouthful of food, but Amy never complained.

"Delicious — just delicious!" she said after every meal.

Dee moved his insurance office back to the house in order to be nearby to help. They now had to lift Amy into a chair when they made her bed. Amy had to be confined to her bed at all times, although they did carry her downstairs for Christmas.

Kathleen had helped Robert pick out a flannel robe for her as a present. Robert loved bright red. No other color would do.

"This is for *you*, Amy," he said slowly as if to a little

child as he handed her the present. Granddaughter Amy, home on vacation from journalism school, opened the box for her grandmother and put the bright robe around her.

"I think she knows you gave it to her, Father," Kathleen said.

Robert and the others said to her: "Nanny-goat" — their nickname for her — "Nanny-goat, you're the grandest tiger in the jungle!"

Amy laughed. She tried hard to be a part of the family as they laughed and talked; she tried bravely to enter into their play.

When spring came and the time to take off for Ludington, Dee and young Bob made a bed in the back of the car. They carried Amy out and lifted her into the improvised bed.

"She looks comfortable," said Bob.

"You know, I really think she knows where we're going," said Dee.

That evening, after five hundred miles of driving, Bob lifted his grandmother out of the car.

"Bob," she said to her grandson as he held her, "How much longer is this performance going to go on?"

"We're at Epworth, Nanny-goat!" said Bob.

The exhilarating fresh breezes off the lake seemed to give Amy new energy at first, but soon she began again to fail noticeably.

One day, Robert heard Amy, all alone in her room, chattering to herself. The family had become accustomed to such chattering and generally paid no attention to it, but on this particular day, Robert went in to her room. Even in her bewildered state, Amy occasionally responded to her name.

Robert leaned toward her and said, "Amy . . . Amy . . . Amy." Finally, she turned her sightless eyes toward him.

"What is it?" she asked.

"Who were you jabbering at?"

"I was jabbering at you," she said.

"But, Amy, that's no way for you to talk," Robert said, smiling. "Don't you realize that I am a holy bishop?"

"Oh, phooey!" said Amy.

As Kathleen said later, Amy seemed proud that her husband had become a bishop, but to her he was always still the young poet-dreamer who had come so simply to Junction City many years before and rowed the borrowed flat-bottom boat on long summer evenings.

The doctor came to Robert the next morning. "Bishop, I'm afraid your wife is very near the end now. She had a very bad night," he said. "By artificial means, I can galvanize her, as it were, and sustain her for a little while, but the decision is up to you. She will suffer, if I do."

Robert stood staring at the floor.

"Don't misunderstand me," the doctor continued. "We'll do everything we can to keep her alive. We'll do what we can in any case, but I doubt that stimulating her by artificial means would prolong her life more than a few days at the most. But the decision is up to you."

Robert looked up. "It is not a hard decision," he said. "Mrs. Spencer has told me over and over again, 'Robert, there is a tug-of-war between your prayers and mine. You're praying that I stay here, and I'm praying that I go.' She's said that to me dozens of times. I think that makes it clear what way we should do, don't you? I certainly know if somebody were bolstering me up into a condition of pain when there was no necessity for it, I'd say, like

Frederick Robinson, 'Stand aside from me, and let God do His work.'"

"I'm glad you made that decision," said the doctor, "because we'd be stimulating only a mere semblance of life."

For a few days more, they kept Amy home by the lake. Finally, early one evening they moved her to the hospital, hoping to make the labored breathing easier for her.

Less than an hour later, Robert, Kathleen, Dee, and the grandchildren stood by her bed. Amy had taken one final breath, and the long-abused heart stopped at last.

For a moment they just stood there. No one wept. The nurse seemed electrified by the composure of that family group as she watched them.

"Apparently, someone has prepared all of you for this experience," she said as they stepped out into the hall. "I've never witnessed such a scene in all my years of nursing. I mean it — you have been a real inspiration to me."

Robert and Kathleen went to make arrangements for the funeral. Dee and the grandchildren, Amy and Bob, went back to the resort.

At ten o'clock Bob returned to his job at the hotel. "I know Nanny would have wanted me to," he said. And young Amy, who was working on the local paper, wrote up her grandmother's death. Her story was picked up by the Associated Press. "How pleased Nanny-goat would have been!" she said.

The Reverend Roy Gregg, a longtime friend and summer neighbor, conducted Amy's funeral in the little church at Ludington.

That next Sunday was Robert's annual day to preach at Epworth, and he spoke twice. In the morning he spoke on immortality at a service at which all of Amy's favorite hymns were sung.

"At Eastertime we read the Gospel reminder of our immortality," he said. "It is the story of a disciple's faith: 'Then went in also that other disciple, which came first to the sepulchre, and he saw, and believed.'"

"What did he see?" he continued. "He did not see then the risen Lord, not any more than you or I. He saw the napkin that had been over the dead face of the Lord, saw it carefully folded and lying in a place by itself. And that tiny thing made him believe! Whatever else he writes, he must write that, to be the Gospel for the glad new morning. A tranquillity after victory over death! That is what it means."

Robert looked down at Kathleen sitting in the congregation. "Have we seen it? How many times on the faces of the dead! How many times have we heard: 'How peaceful he looks!' 'How peaceful she looks!' *That*, of course, is the folded napkin in the Garden of the Resurrection."

Friends had turned out in droves for the morning service, to pay final tribute to a beloved neighbor who had left them.

That evening Robert preached again, this time at vespers on the beach. He gave a talk about Epworth Heights and its history.

"Here in this Place of Light," he said, "I have often seen the lights go out in the homes of Ludington, but there was always one light that burned on steadily the whole night on. It is the light at the harbor's entrance. However automatically it is managed, there has to be a keeper, and the keeper knows it is not his light. He must keep it burning, knowing 'the earnest expectation of the ships.' "

The DeYongs were driving to Kansas City the next day, but Robert wished to accompany the casket and so took the train.

As he told the family later, he sat up in the Vista-Dome and looked down at the baggage car just three cars ahead. On that return trip, Robert said, he relived in his mind the early days when they had gone boating at Junction City, the many Saturdays through the years that he had read sermons to her as she sewed and made her "infallibly wise" criticisms.

"And I thanked God for all the years of devoted companionship," he said. "You know, Kathleen, I guess I really did sum up what your mother meant to me in *The Seer's House.* I said that in the darkness and in the light your mother interpreted to me the meaning of the saints."

Back at Kansas City, Robert put his one pair of summer trousers on the line. Baron, a neighbors' dog, came over, pulled them down, and tore them to shreds.

"Oh, Bishop!" the neighbors exclaimed. "Oh, Bishop, we're mortified about the trousers. Baron never —"

"Please don't 'Oh, Bishop' me," said Robert. "That dog didn't know I was a holy man!"

He went upstairs and put on the only pair he could find, a woolen pair which was riddled with moth holes. He looked at himself in the full-length mirror, saw the holes, and decided to try pulling them together with adhesive tape.

"But, Father!" Kathleen shrieked, pointing to the one large hole Robert had missed.

Robert disappeared for a moment, took the cork from a black ink bottle and inked his knee underneath. No one who showed up for the interment seemed to notice the camouflage.

Dr. Trelease from St. Paul's Church took the service, but Robert insisted on saying a few words.

"I know that Amy in her paradise would wish me to thank you for coming out to this service today," said Robert; "and I, too, thank you. . . . When I reminded my Amy just before she died that I was a holy bishop, she said, 'Oh, phooey!' So you see, she really was not out of her mind when she left us at the end."

Back at home, Robert's grace at dinner seemed longer than usual.

"Why such a long grace, Gaga?" young Amy asked.

"If I made my grace as short as the one in the prayer book," said Robert, "it wouldn't give Him time to get off the other phone!"

But silently, then and daily forever since, Robert added words they did not hear: *And may our Amy ever enjoy the food and the refreshment of Thine everlasting Kingdom.*

CHAPTER XXX

"Well?"

SUCH HAS BEEN THE LIFE of Robert Nelson Spencer, a man of great humor and compassion, a man of fierce courage and spiritual insight, a man of whimsy and fine talent and achievement that could be counted in citations — in lives touched and made better by him.

At St. John's, Springfield, the people have named their parish hall for him. At Ludington, one summer, they held a "Bishop Robert Nelson Spencer Day" when from all over the country messages poured in from friends like Dr. Fred O'Donnell of Junction City, Rabbi Mayerberg, and Harry S. Truman, whose daughter Robert had confirmed.

When the people of West Missouri voted Robert an annuity, they gave their gift in this form, they said, to keep him from giving it all away to others, as he was prone to do.

"I know there is love behind this, a love which I do not deserve, but for which I am overwhelmingly grateful," he said when he accepted the gift. "Perhaps I have been arrogant at times, or have tried to have my way too much, but God knows I have wanted to be humble. Christianity is nothing if it does not teach us how to live with one another."

In his room Robert keeps piles of speech notes, clippings,

letters, and old photographs in large cartons. Theological books fill two rooms and line the hall. His books have overflowed the bookshelves and are now stacked high on the floor of his room. Propped up against the wall, behind one such pile, is his Consecration Certificate in its old frame. In another corner stands an autographed picture of Edwin Markham. On the back of the door, two old worn cassocks hang from a hook.

Occasionally, Robert is called on to give the Invocation or Blessing at a public dinner, or to be — as he puts it — the "locomotive" or "caboose." From time to time, his successor, keen-witted Bishop Edward Welles, asks him to take confirmations.

"Don't call me a retired bishop," he says. "I loathe the term. Say 'Bishop Spencer, Long Time No See'!"

How will Robert Nelson Spencer be remembered in years to come? As a man whose courage could meet the tests of physical suffering and gangsters' threats, a man whose graceful humor brightened sober meetings and even somber pages of the *Star*, a man whose poetry was music and whose prose was poetry?

Will he be remembered as "Roaring Bob" of the Preaching Mission days, or as a man of rare compassion who seemed always able to "love the unlovable and forgive the unforgiveable," and who radiated wherever he went a kind of firsthand knowledge of his Lord?

Or will he be remembered by the Missourians he loved and served as a man whose very life showed that the Gospel of Jesus Christ first preached long ago had relevance to a perplexing age of nuclear weapons and widespread tensions? It will be interesting to see.

Not long ago, Robert told a friend, "You know, I have

the feeling that Billy Graham wants me to think that flames will be lapping around my ankles at the last. I have nothing against Billy Graham, I'm all for him, but I think he's wrong about that! I don't believe there will be flames. Somehow, I think Studdert-Kennedy had it right when he had his cockney soldier say:

> There ain't no throne, and there ain't no books
>   It's 'Im you've got to see,
> It's 'Im, just 'Im that is the Judge
>   Of blokes like you and me.
>
> And, boys, I'd sooner frizzle up
>   I' the flames of a burnin' 'Ell
> Than stand and look into 'Is face,
>   And 'ear 'Is voice say — "Well?"